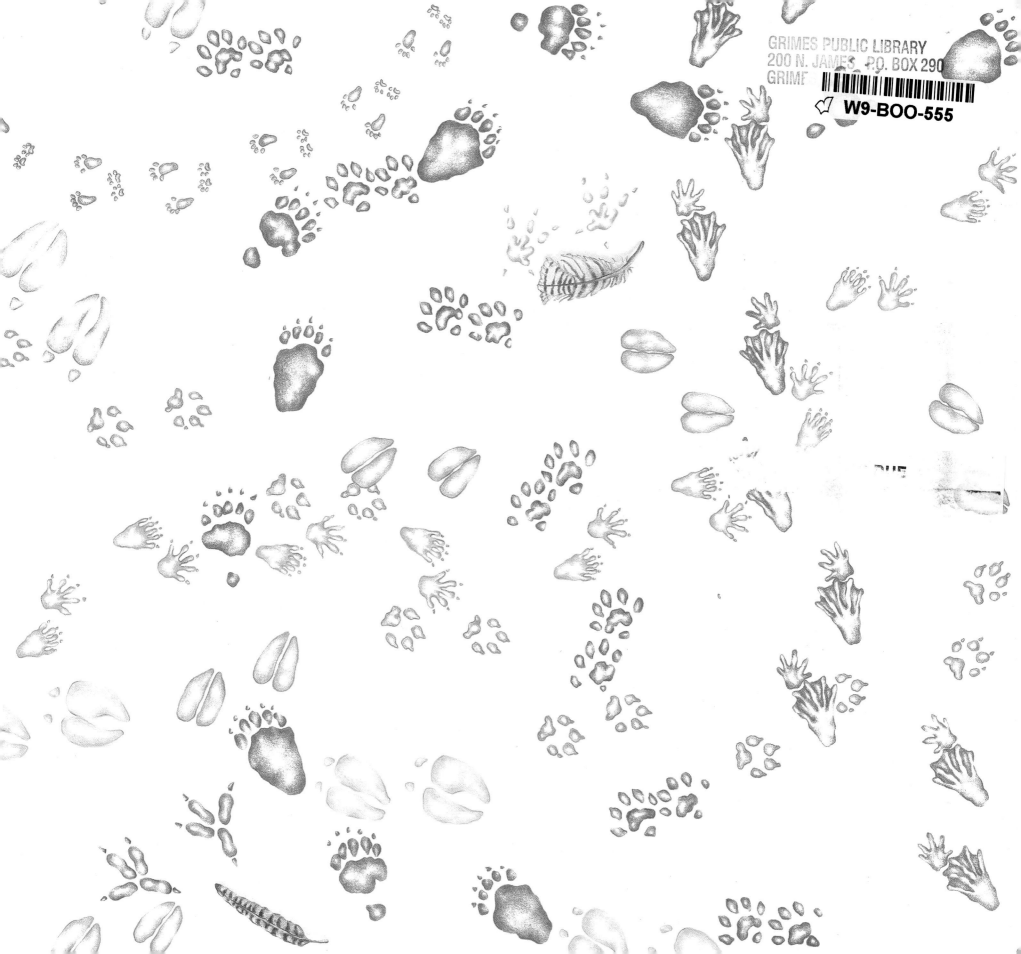

Once Upon a Rainbow

Once Upon a Rainbow

WRITTEN AND ILLUSTRATED BY

Jennifer Woods Tierney

HONEYSUCKLE PRESS

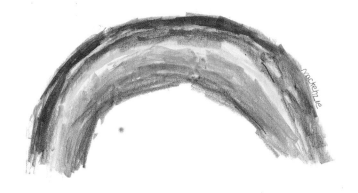

Dedicated to

Jessica and Mackenzie

Remembering

my grandparents and Peach

Once upon a beaver pond,
there lived an otter who was fond
of lily pads and dragonflies,
and playing under clear blue skies.

Mazie was her name and she had webbed feet,
a tail for a rudder so long and sleek.
She chased the fish and played tag with frogs.
She napped with turtles on warm, sunny logs.

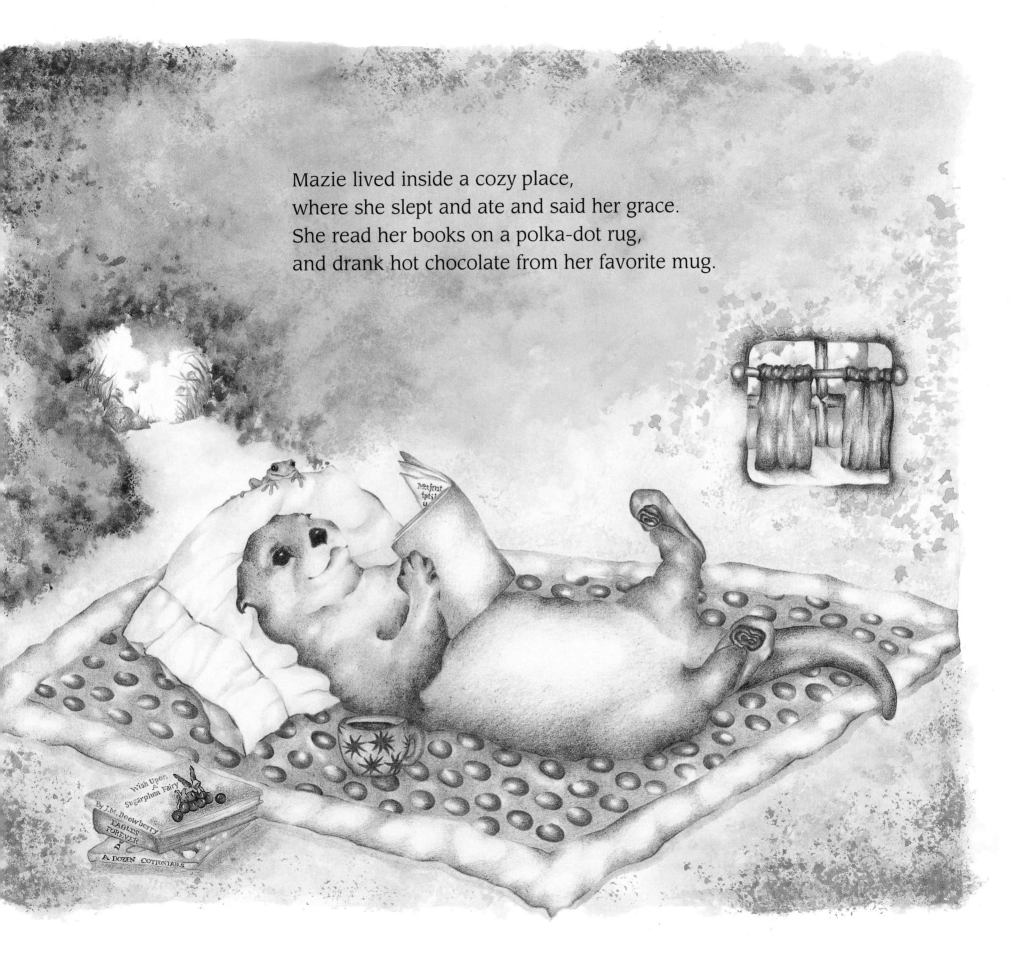

Mazie lived inside a cozy place,
where she slept and ate and said her grace.
She read her books on a polka-dot rug,
and drank hot chocolate from her favorite mug.

Playing with her sister was best of all,
as she'd race her down the waterfall.
Follow-the-leader through tall cattails,
was almost as fun as diving for snails.
Her favorite game was hide-and-seek.
She'd count to ten and hardly peek.

The muddy banks made a perfect slide.
Fast as lightning, down she'd glide!
She loved her friends and her family too,
and helping her mommy make crayfish stew.

One stormy day dark clouds rolled by,
and raindrops splish-splashed from the sky.
After the storm came a magical sight,
filled with color and filled with light.
It arched high above the golden sun.
Mazie counted the colors
    one by one.

A dazzling rainbow lit up the sky,
like fireworks on the Fourth of July.
It stretched from the heavens right down to the ground.
Mazie wanted to know where the end could be found.
Where did it come from? Where did it go?
Could she find out? Would anyone know?

She asked her mommy where the rainbow led,
and this is what her mommy said,
"Rainbows are nature's magic and wonder.
They follow the lightning and chase away thunder.
And far at the end is a secret treasure,
something so special
    it can't be measured.
Maybe if you go and
    ask your friends,
they'll know what's hidden
    at the rainbow's end."

Mazie was off and well on her way,
without even a snack or a word to say.
She raced and slid through the tall fireweed,
with a trail of pink petals and going top speed!
Chances seemed good that Deer would know.
Her ears were so sharp she could hear falling snow.
At this time of the day Mazie knew where to look.
She'd be getting a drink in the cool mountain brook.

Before a pink petal could float to the ground,
her good friend Deer had already been found.
"I'm wondering, Deer, do you happen to know,
what's at the end of the magic rainbow?"

"I think there are meadows always in spring,
where clover grows wild and birds always sing.
Or maybe an orchard forever in bloom,
with fruit sweet and ripe that smells like perfume!
I wonder what our friend Fox has to say.
I think she's asleep on the hillside today.
Foxes are clever, as everyone knows.
She'll have an answer, don't you suppose?"

Up the hill she went, straight to the top,
and tumbled to a stop with a big belly flop.
"I wonder, Fox, do you happen to know,
what's at the end of the magic rainbow?"
Her good friend Fox opened one sleepy eye,
let out a yawn, and then gave her reply.

"Maybe the rainbow could round up the stars,
harness the moon, and then lasso Mars.
They'd form a bright nightlight, only for me,
to shine on my path and help me to see.
For what's more fun than playing all night,
and snapping at fireflies till morning's first light?
But I would ask Beaver, if it were me.
I think he stops work at a quarter to three."

Splash went the water and away Mazie swam,
Heading upstream to the neighborhood dam.
And there sat Beaver on a big pile of sticks,
with a hole in his roof that he really should fix.
Beavers work hard every day of the year.
Come rain or come shine, he's a real engineer.
"I wonder, Beaver, do you happen to know,
what's at the end of the magic rainbow?"

Beaver thought hard for a moment or two.
"I think it's a home that is sturdy and new,
without anything broken or needing repair.
I could take a day off and not even care!
I wish you could stay and play some today,
but why not find out what Bear has to say?
He passed this way about an hour ago,
looking for blueberries, don't you know.
You will have to hurry, you mustn't be late.
For Bear's getting ready to hibernate."

Mazie found Bear with blue on his paws,
blue on his nose, and blue on his claws.
"I wonder, Bear, do you happen to know,
what's at the end of the magic rainbow?"
As the scent of autumn leaves drifted on air,
a smile spread across the face of that bear.

"There's a cave warm and cozy with leaves thick and deep,
to doze off all winter in a long peaceful sleep!"
Mazie thought Bear's idea sounded real swell.
So she gave him her thanks and then said farewell!

As she drifted downstream she gazed overhead,
wondering about what her good friends had said.
Fireflies and starlight . . . leaves and sweet clover . . .
she drifted along while thinking it over.
If she had bright balloons to lift her up high,
she could see rainbow's end from up in the sky.

But oh dear me, it was getting late,
and giving up was just not her trait.
With the sun sinking low in the western sky,
Mazie had to give it just one last try.
But she had no balloons, so what could she do?
Perhaps she could ask someone who flew.
And that's when she saw him soaring so high,
a pair of huge wings against the blue sky.

Owl circled just once and then down he dove,
landing nearby in a tall aspen grove.
"I wonder, Owl, do you happen to know,
what's at the end of the magic rainbow?"
He blinked his big eyes, once and then twice,
and next offered Mazie his wisest advice.

"Everyone seems to have their own view,
so let's find out what is true for you.
If you'll follow me, my curious friend,
we'll learn what's at *your* rainbow's end!"

Owl's hoot echoed throughout the land,
calling on friends to give Mazie a hand.
They came from the north, the south, east and west.
They came all that way without even a rest.

One by one the friends stacked up high,
from tallest to smallest right into the sky.
There was Moose on the bottom and Eagle on top,
Raccoon in the middle holding Fox up.
Elk watched as Mazie climbed toward the moon,
and Chipmunk cheered on, "You'll be there soon!"

That's when the rainbow swept Mazie away,
and down she slid on the shimmering rays!
She slipped and she flipped and did somersaults.
She hopped and she skipped and did a quick waltz!
She tumbled and twirled, then all in a flash,
plunged into the water with one giant splash!

When she opened her eyes, what did she see?
She was back in her pond with her whole family.
Mommy and daddy were there, and her sister too.
Mazie had gone a long way to find out what's true.

Her friends and her family were what mattered most.
She'd found rainbow's end, she finally could boast.
The magic rainbow had now faded away,
but the treasure it left would be here to stay.
Mazie was home at last with the polka-dot rug,
and there in the corner was her favorite mug.
She was just in time for milk and prayers,
and for Daddy to tuck her in bed upstairs.

The rainbow had carried her home that night,
to Mommy's arms, now holding her tight.
Home where Daddy would always tuck her in bed,
and she'd snuggle up close while Mommy read.
So, when Mazie closed her eyes that night,
in the flickering glow of the candlelight,
she had no doubt that she had found,
her favorite treasure the whole world round.

THE END

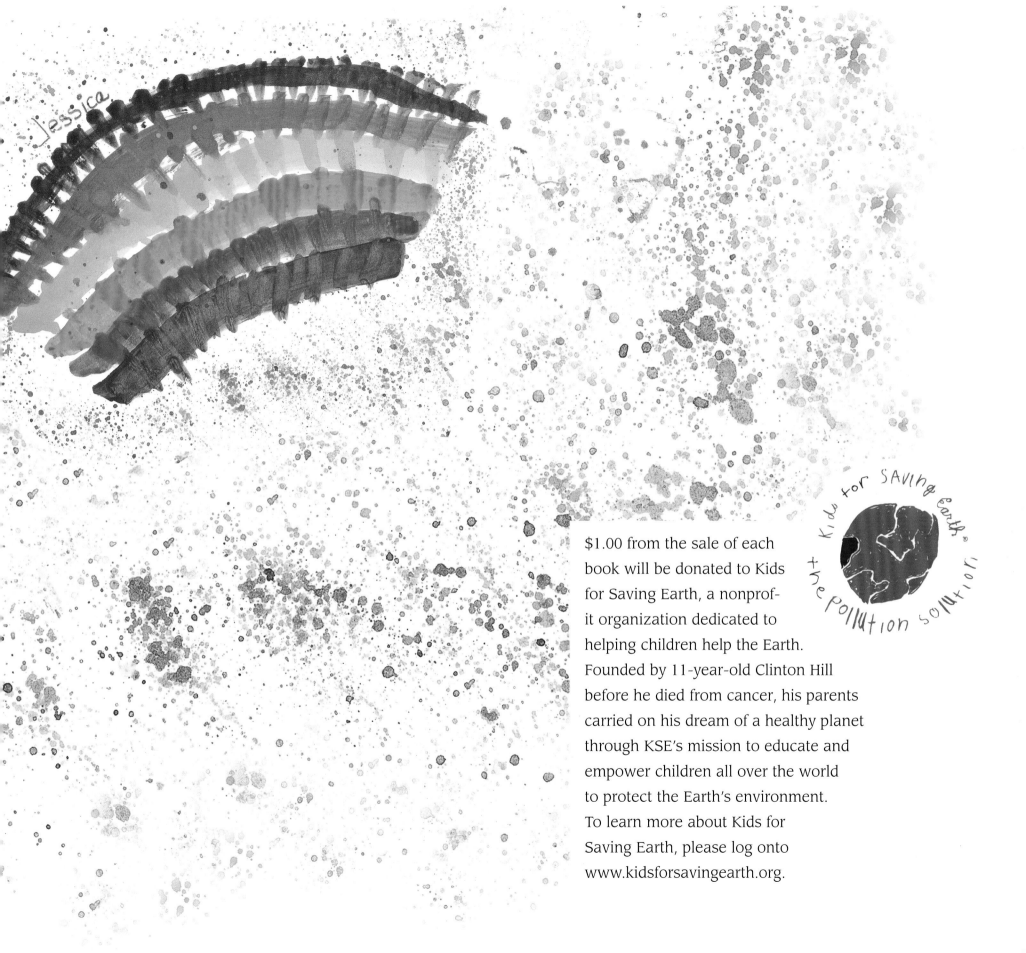

Jessica

Kids for Saving Earth
the Pollution solution

$1.00 from the sale of each book will be donated to Kids for Saving Earth, a nonprofit organization dedicated to helping children help the Earth. Founded by 11-year-old Clinton Hill before he died from cancer, his parents carried on his dream of a healthy planet through KSE's mission to educate and empower children all over the world to protect the Earth's environment. To learn more about Kids for Saving Earth, please log onto www.kidsforsavingearth.org.

RIVER OTTERS are champion swimmers and can hold their breath underwater for up to eight minutes. They have natural nose plugs—special muscles they close when diving to the bottom of rivers and ponds to search for food. Otters use their webbed feet like paddles and their powerful tails like a rudder to steer. They even know several different swimming strokes. Their oily fur is waterproof and dense—with as many as one million hairs per square inch! Otters love to play and spend endless hours sliding down riverbanks, then racing to the top to slide down again.

BEAVERS are nature's builders. Using long teeth to chew through wood, they cut down trees and branches to build a lodge. If a tree trunk is heavy, they work together to drag it to the water and float it to their building site, usually in a river or pond. They stack logs, sticks, and branches into a big mound and pack on mud to hold it together. Then they chew through the wood to make an underwater entrance and also a room where the beaver family will live in the safety of its lodge.

DEER feed in the early morning and early evening. They nibble grasses and leaves, twigs, and branches—sometimes standing on their hind legs to reach up high. Deer eat quickly and swallow their food almost whole. Later they find a safe place to lie down to chew it. Deer are ruminants, or cud chewers, and have a special kind of stomach where food is stored and softened. The deer then brings up a wad of partly digested food, called a cud, and chews it completely before swallowing it again and digesting it fully.

BALD EAGLES soar through the sky, spreading their wings and tail feathers to ride warm air as it rises. Bald eagles build nests high up in trees or on rocky cliffs, usually along rivers, lakes, seacoasts, or other wetland areas where fish are plentiful. The male and female raise their young together. While the mother protects the nest, the father searches for food, using his keen eyesight to spot fish, small rodents, and mammals. When he spots prey, he swoops down at speeds of more than 100 miles per hour. He then returns to the nest to feed the family.

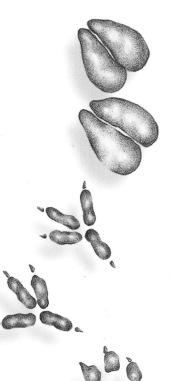

RED FOX pups are born in the spring, when the mother fox gives birth to a litter of two to ten pups. Both parents help care for them. The pups are helpless and do not leave the den at first. When they are about two months old, they start to venture out from the den. Fox pups love to nap in the sun and play. They crouch and pounce, they stalk and chase and wrestle each other. This play is good practice for hunting. When they are about six months old, the young foxes will live and hunt on their own.

BLACK BEARS hibernate when the weather turns cold, settling into a den to sleep through the winter. When they emerge from hibernation in spring, they are hungry and start foraging for food. Bears are omnivores, meaning they will eat almost anything. They feed on berries and nuts, as well as roots, bark, eggs, insects, fish, and mammals. And, yes, bears love honey! With their keen sense of smell, bears can sniff out food three miles away. Come late summer and early fall, black bears eat heavily to fatten up again for their long winter sleep.

RACCOONS are curious and playful and often get into mischief. With nimble fingers they can open latches, unscrew jars, and lift trash can lids to eat food scraps. Their bandit-mask markings make them look like thieves in the night. Raccoons live in cities and suburbs, but thrive in natural areas where they dwell in hollow trees near streams, marshes, and woodland ponds. Raccoons have a puzzling habit of washing their food in water before eating it. Scientists are not sure why raccoons do this. Maybe they just like to play with their food!

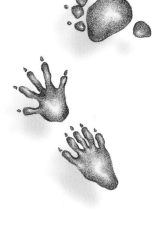

BARRED OWLS have large round eyes that look straight ahead. To see from side to side, an owl must turn its entire head. The owl's sharp eyesight and keen hearing make it an excellent hunter. When it sees or hears prey, the owl quietly swoops down to catch it. Specially shaped wing feathers allow the bird to fly silently as it hunts. People, however, are more likely to hear an owl than see it. The owl's plumage blends into the surroundings as it sleeps during the day. But at night the owl hoots, hoots, hoots.

MOOSE are very big animals. An adult male may stand more than seven feet tall at the shoulders and weigh over 1,500 pounds. Because it has large hooves, a moose can walk over marshy ground without sinking. In summer it likes to wade into ponds, rivers, and swampy areas to feed. Dipping its head underwater, a moose uses its lips to feel around for pond weeds, water lilies, and other aquatic plants. Holding its breath and using its hooves to swim, a moose can dive deep—up to 18 feet!—to find its favorite plants.

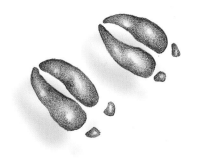

ELK are social animals and live together in herds. Female elk, called cows, live in herds with their young. There can be as many as 400 animals in a herd. Male elk, called bulls, live in smaller bachelor herds. During the fall mating season, bulls call to females by "bugling" and fight other males for dominance. Cows usually give birth to one calf in the spring. Rising up on wobbly legs, a newborn calf can stand within a half hour of being born. It stays close to its mother for the first few weeks and then joins the rest of the herd.

Honeysuckle Press
3855 Pleasant Ridge Road
Boulder, CO 80301
www.honeysucklepresscolorado.com

ISBN 0-9787716-0-5

Editing support: Thank you Foothill Elementary School students, Suzanne Venino, Kerry Lee MacLean,
Susan Leibfritz, Nancy Libbey Mills, Terry Tierney, Katie Callender, and Christina Burress.

Gratitude: A really big thank you to Foothill Elementary School students and teachers for helping me write my first children's book.
Thank you to all the children and my friends at Mapleton Montessori School. Deep thanks to Dr. Carole Christensen and my friends in
the New Life Center at Avista Hospital. Heartfelt thanks to Barbara Russell, Kathleen Eakins, Suzanne Simons, Barbara Mahler, Michael
Smith, Dan Cox, my friends at In Motion Rehabilitation, Phoenix Wellness Center, Integrated Healthcare, Center IMT, Principled
Chiropractic, and to each and every one who gave me support and encouragement along the way. A special kind of thanks to my Mom
and Dad for many things, and to my sister and brother for fireflies and mud slides. Thank you is not enough to Jess and Kenz for being
to my left and to my right, for being my teachers and my joy. And to you, Ter, my best friend, for making all my dreams come true.

The text type of this book is set in ITC Leawood.
The illustrations are rendered in watercolor, oil pencils, and chalk pastels.

Produced by Boulder Bookworks, Boulder, Colorado
Printed in Canada

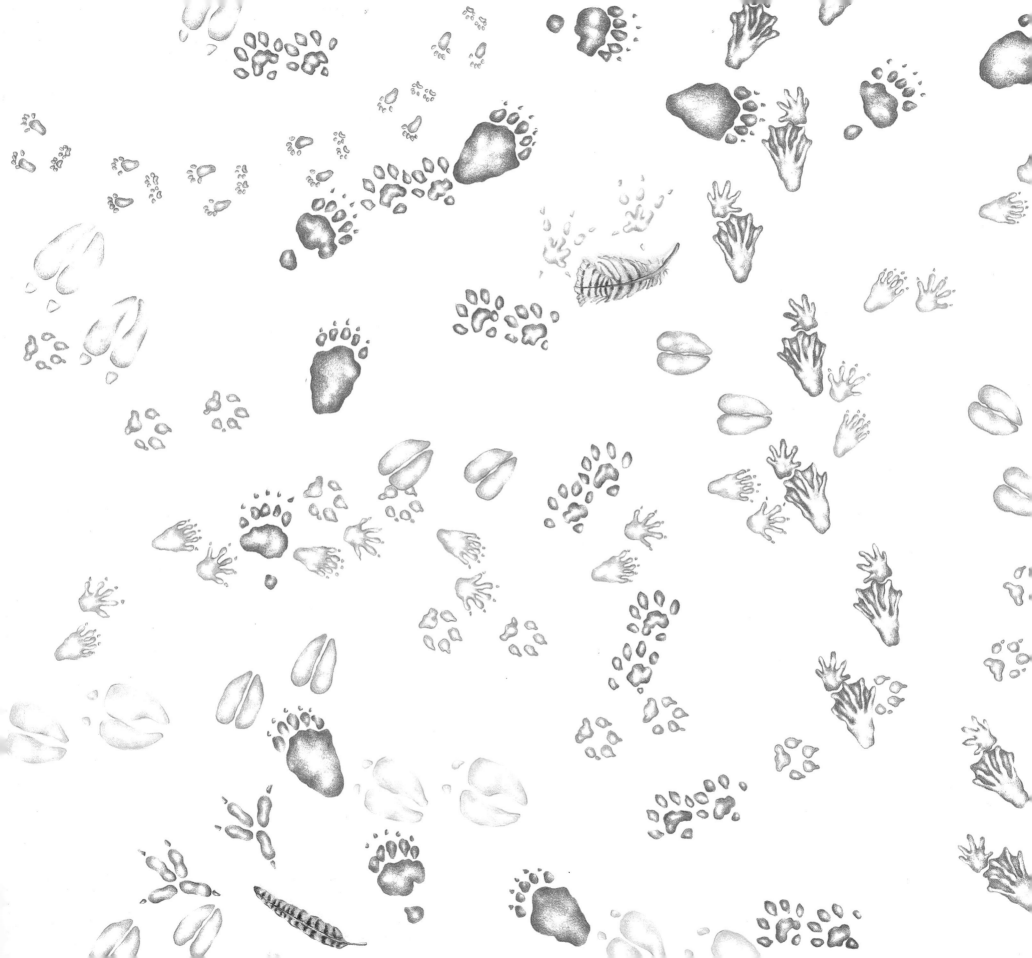

A SOLDIER'S LIFE

A Visual History of Soldiers Through the Ages

Andrew Robertshaw

Lodestar Books
Dutton   New York

*"Soldiers, like other men, found more hard
work than glory in their calling."*

Frederic Remington

First published in the United States in 1997 by
Lodestar Books, an affiliate of Dutton Children's Books,
a division of Penguin Books USA Inc.,
375 Hudson Street, New York, New York 10014

Library of Congress Cataloging-in-Publication Data

Robertshaw, Andrew
  A Soldier's Life: a visual history of soldiers through the ages/
Andrew Robertshaw.—1st American ed.
    p. cm.
  Includes index.
  ISBN 0-525-67550-7 (alk. paper)
  1. Soldiers—History—Pictorial works. 2. Military supplies—
Pictorial works. I. Title.
U750.R63 1997
355.02'09—dc20

                                            96-44309 CIP

Originally published in Great Britain in 1997 by Heinemann Children's Reference,
an imprint of Heinemann Educational Publishers,
a division of Reed Educational and Professional Publishing Ltd.,
Halley Court, Jordan Hill, Oxford, OX2 8EJ

Printed in Hong Kong
First American Edition
ISBN: 0-525-67550-7
10 9 8 7 6 5 4 3 2 1

Conceived and produced by Breslich & Foss, Ltd. London
Series Editor: Laura Wilson
Editorial Assistant: Elizabeth Haylett
Art Director: Nigel Osborne
Design: Margaret Sadler
Photography: Miki Slingsby

CONTENTS

ROMAN SOLDIERS c.50 A.D.

Legionary Julius Favonius Facilus and Auxiliary Marcus Brigionus

At its height, the Roman Empire extended from southern Scotland to the Sahara Desert, and from Syria in the east to Spain in the west. It lasted more than one thousand years, and for most of that time, the Romans were fighting somewhere in the empire, either to gain new territory or to keep control of conquered territory.

The Roman army succeeded in this because it was very powerful and well organized. It consisted of nearly 30 legions, which were groups of 5,000 infantrymen and supporting cavalrymen. The legions were divided into groups of 80 to100 men, which were called centuries. Each century was divided into *contubernia*, or messes, which were groups of 8 soldiers who ate and slept together, sharing a tent and cooking equipment, and sharing rations.

BELOW: *Oil lamp and leather purse. In the first century A.D., legionaries were paid 225* denarii *(silver pieces) per year, and auxiliaries were paid 150* denarii.

RECRUITMENT

Julius joined the army when he was 18. As a Roman citizen, he was able to become a legionary. Like all soldiers, Julius has enlisted for 25 years. He may not marry during his service, but his pay is better than many civilians'. When he leaves, he will be given land and money.

Marcus was not a Roman citizen but a Belgian, so he became an auxiliary (see page 46), not a legionary. When he finishes his service, Marcus and his children will get Roman citizenship. Auxiliaries were sent abroad to serve, in case they were more loyal to their own country than to Rome. They came from all over the empire—many who served on Hadrian's Wall in northern England came from Germany and France.

Soldiers on the march carried tools and cooking equipment as well as their weapons. Since they marched as much as 25 miles a day, their caligae *(hobnailed sandals) were a very important part of their equipment.*

RIGHT: *Julius has* lorica segmentata *(jointed plate armor) over his tunic. Marcus is wearing mail armor.*

RIGHT: *Marcus's belt with his protective bronze apron,* gladius *(short sword),* and *pugio (dagger) in its scabbard*

FIGHTING

Roman soldiers were highly disciplined in battle. They formed ranks facing the enemy and threw their *pila* (javelins). Then, keeping in their ranks and protecting themselves with their shields, they fought with their swords.

The Romans developed military tactics for different situations. For example, if they were besieging a town, they formed a *testudo* (tortoise). A group of soldiers stood close together, with the men on the outside holding their shields by their sides and those in the middle holding their shields flat above their heads to protect them from above. In this way, all the soldiers defended one another, and provided they stayed in the formation, it was hard to stop them from moving forward.

Roman army rations included grain, which one of the men in the contubernium *would grind into flour with a millstone, as well as cheese, meat, and vinegary wine.*

VIKING WARRIOR c.1000 A.D.
Herstein, Son of Asmund

Herstein is wearing linen trousers and two tunics, one linen and one woolen. These are the only clothes he will take to war, and he will not be able to change them for months. He will use his woolen cloak as a blanket. Here, Herstein puts on the leather boots that he will need for the march ahead.

Herstein has a shield, but because he is poor, his only weapons are an axe and a knife. When Viking warriors prepared for battle, they stood close together so that their shields overlapped and formed a wall to protect them from spears (see below).

LEFT: In return for his service, Herstein will receive pay and the loan of a mail shirt, a helmet (see opposite), and two spears like these. Soldiers were supposed to have as many as four spears and a sword, but most could not afford them. Swords were very expensive and not often used.

It is the summer of 1013 A.D., and Herstein is preparing to join the army. Fifty years ago, Herstein's grandfather came to England from Denmark as part of a Viking raiding party. He decided to stay in England and make it his home. Herstein's grandfather was a heathen, who believed in many different gods. Herstein and his father, like a number of Vikings born in England, are Christian, and they speak English, not Danish. Herstein still considers himself a Viking, though his loyalty is to the leader of his village, who has chosen him to fight in the Anglo-Saxon army of the English king,

Ethelred, who is trying to stop a new invasion of heathen Vikings led by King Sveinn of Denmark. Herstein is a farmer, but everyone expects him to become a warrior when he joins up with the band of men chosen by his village, who will march north to the place where the invaders have landed. Although Herstein is 30 years old, he has not been a warrior before, so he hopes that there will be time for him and the other men to practice using their weapons before the battle starts. In spite of his lack of experience, he is very pleased to have the chance to gain honor by serving his leader.

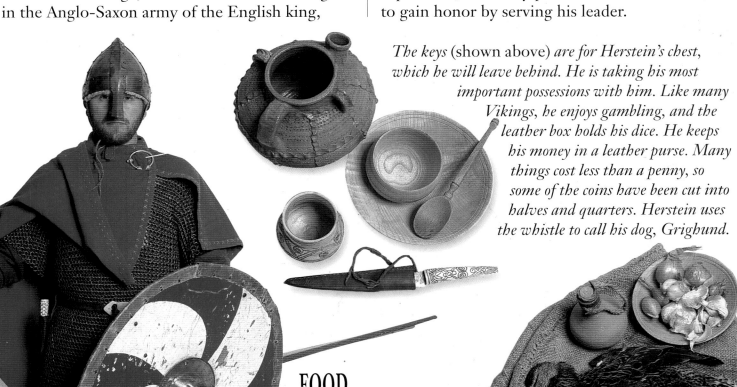

The keys (shown above) *are for Herstein's chest, which he will leave behind. He is taking his most important possessions with him. Like many Vikings, he enjoys gambling, and the leather box holds his dice. He keeps his money in a leather purse. Many things cost less than a penny, so some of the coins have been cut into halves and quarters. Herstein uses the whistle to call his dog, Grighund.*

FOOD

Herstein will not carry breakable pottery cups and jars with him, but he is taking ash wood bowls and cups. He uses the knife for farmwork and to eat with, and he also uses it as a weapon. Herstein will have to find his own food, but he can trap birds, like this duck, and make a porridge from oats, rye, and barley.

Herstein in full battle dress. His cloak is fastened with a silver brooch.

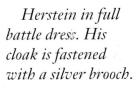

LIGHTING FIRES

Fire-lighting equipment (left). *To produce a flame, Herstein holds a flint in one hand and strikes it on the edge of a piece of steel so that sparks fall onto a piece of dry horse hoof or tinder fungus. When this begins to glow, Herstein touches it with some linen, which bursts into flame.*

THE NORMAN CONQUEST 1066

Drogo FitzPoyntz (Knight) and Robert, son of John (Archer)

In 911, the French king gave some land to the Vikings in order to prevent them from attacking his territory. They settled in France and became known as Normans (Northmen). The part of France where they lived was called Normandy. Like all Vikings who settled abroad, they took up local ways, names, and the language, but they continued to invade other countries in order to gain more territory.

The English king, Edward the Confessor, had promised the throne to his cousin Duke William of Normandy. However, when Edward died in 1066, Harold Godwin-sson, a Saxon claimant, was crowned. William's invasion force of more than 7,000 men and horses sailed from France and landed in the south of England. They defeated the Saxons at Hastings, where Harold was killed, and William was crowned king.

ABOVE: *Colored braid for a knight's tunic*

DUKE WILLIAM'S INVASION FORCE

Duke William's invasion force was made up of Norman knights, their followers, and mercenaries. Many knights, like Drogo FitzPoyntz *(shown opposite right)*, had no land in Normandy, but they knew that if William became king of England, he would give them Saxon land as a reward.

Mercenary soldiers like Robert *(shown opposite left)* were given money if a battle was won. Victory often depended on mercenaries. Before the Normans landed in England, the mercenaries heard that food supplies were low, and they threatened to leave. William knew he could not win without them, so he ordered that double rations be given to each man, even though there was little food left. This was a good idea—the mercenaries stayed and the Normans won and took as much food as they wanted from the defeated Saxons.

ABOVE LEFT: *Different-shaped arrows were used for different targets: Narrow-headed ones were used in battle because they could pierce mail, and arrows with broader heads were occasionally used against warhorses in battle but mainly for hunting. Men called fletchers made the fletchings on the ends of arrows out of goose feathers.*

The Normans brought food with them, but they also plundered Saxon farms and villages to feed themselves and their horses.

RIGHT: *Although Saxons hunted with bows and arrows, they did not fight with them. Norman armies included both crossbowmen and archers like Robert, son of John (shown opposite), who could shoot six or seven arrows per minute. They wore thick, padded tunics for protection.*

Drogo FitzPoyntz in full armor. Knights like Drogo wore mail and fought on horseback. The Saxons, like the Vikings, defended themselves with a shield wall. Once it was broken, the Normans were able to defeat them.

SHOOTING AN ARROW

Robert strings his bow with a bowstring.

He draws an arrow. Archers either kept arrows in a quiver (shown here) or stuck them through their belts or into the ground.

He fits the arrow's nock (groove) onto the bowstring.

He aims and draws the bowstring back before shooting the arrow at its target.

RIGHT: Drogo's main weapon was a sword.

THE CRUSADES 1095–*c.*1550

Nicholas d'Artois (Knight) and William Trussel (Crossbowman)

The crusades began in 1095, when Pope Urban II called on Christians to capture the Holy Lands (now Syria and Israel) from the Muslims. He was particularly interested in capturing Jerusalem, the city where Jesus was crucified. The First Crusade began in 1096, and the army took Jerusalem in 1099. During the next eighty years, the Muslim leaders, who previously fought each other, united against the enemy and successfully invaded many of the cities controlled by the crusaders. Despite a Second Crusade in 1147, the army of Saladin, the Muslim sultan, took Jerusalem in 1187. Pope Gregory VIII preached the Third Crusade, and Frederick I Barbarossa, Emperor of Germany; Phillip II of France; and Richard I of England (known as Richard the Lionheart) raised armies and set out for the Holy Lands.

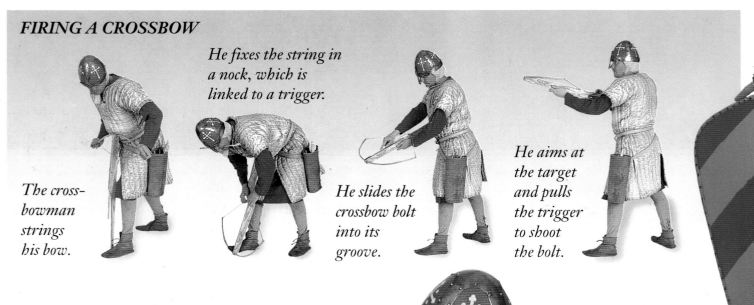

FIRING A CROSSBOW

The cross-bowman strings his bow.

He fixes the string in a nock, which is linked to a trigger.

He slides the crossbow bolt into its groove.

He aims at the target and pulls the trigger to shoot the bolt.

MOTIVES

Many different people went on the crusades, from rich knights such as Nicholas d'Artois, who traveled with servants, to poor craftsmen, who had sold everything in order to raise money for the journey. The Pope had promised that all crusaders' sins, past and future, would be forgiven. At this time, people's belief in God was strong, and the thought that they could be free to behave as they liked without fear of going to hell was very tempting. Although some went for religious reasons, others wanted adventure and the chance to acquire land and treasure. In Europe, land always passed from one eldest son to another, and landless younger sons often became crusaders in the hope of getting some.

William (below) *and Nicholas* (right). *Nicholas has cloth in the shape of a cross on his cloak to show that he is a crusader.*

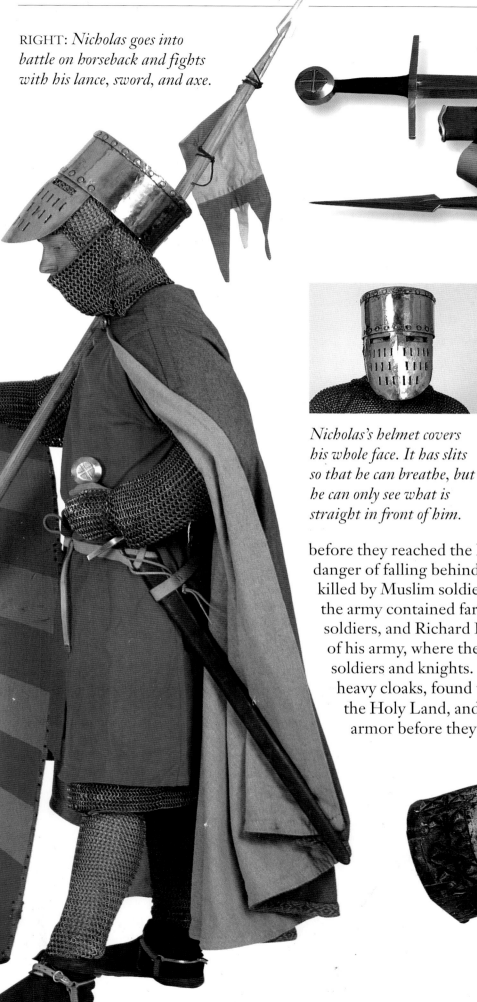

RIGHT: *Nicholas goes into battle on horseback and fights with his lance, sword, and axe.*

Nicholas's helmet covers his whole face. It has slits so that he can breathe, but he can only see what is straight in front of him.

ON THE MARCH

The people who went on the First Crusade didn't know what the Holy Land was like or how far away it was, and few of them lived to return home and tell their stories. Some early crusaders were unarmed and traveled on foot, with little money to buy food, and thousands died of starvation, exhaustion, or disease before they reached the Holy Land. They were also in constant danger of falling behind the mounted crusaders and of being killed by Muslim soldiers. By the time of the Third Crusade, the army contained far more well-armed, experienced soldiers, and Richard I made the civilians travel in the middle of his army, where they were protected by armed foot soldiers and knights. Knights, who wore mail, helmets, and heavy cloaks, found this clothing unbearable in the heat of the Holy Land, and many had sold or thrown away their armor before they reached Jerusalem.

RIGHT: *A rich crusader like Nicholas had plenty of money to feed himself and his servants, to pay for his horse to be shod, and to have his armor mended.*

WARS OF THE ROSES 1455-85

Sir Thomas Burgh (Man-at-Arms), Richard Calle (Archer), and Edmund Clere (Billman)

The two most powerful families in England, both of whom had a legal claim to the throne, fought for more than 30 years over who should rule. These battles are now called the Wars of the Roses because one side, the House of Lancaster, had a red rose as its symbol, and the other side, the House of York, had a white rose. The Wars of the Roses eventually came to an end when Henry Tudor defeated the Yorkist King Richard III at the battle of Bosworth in 1485. Richard III was killed in the battle, and Henry Tudor was crowned Henry VII.

Sir Thomas Burgh is a supporter of the house of York. He is a Knight Bannerette, which means that he has special permission to display his own banner (flag) when he goes into battle. Like some Yorkists, Sir Thomas had to change sides quickly after the battle of Bosworth, but he was luckier than many because he found favor with the new king. A lot of Yorkist noblemen had their money and land taken away, and some were executed or sent into exile.

RIGHT: *Sir Thomas pays two of his soldiers, Richard Calle the archer (kneeling) and Edmund Clere, who is a billman (standing).*

ABOVE: *Sword and arrows. There were differently shaped arrowheads for different functions (see page 8). Knights like Sir Thomas Burgh did not usually fight on horseback but rode to the battlefield, dismounted, and fought on foot. There was not much fancy swordplay in the thick of battle—soldiers simply tried to slash or beat their opponents to death with any weapon that was available.*

WEAPONS

Battles during the Wars of the Roses began with a bombardment of arrows. The bow and arrow was the chief weapon for poor men, and there were more archers in the army than any other type of soldier. As well as arrows, there were also cannons and handguns, although these were very crude, with matchlock mechanisms (*see page 15*). They were, however, very popular with noblemen, who spent large amounts of money buying as many guns as they could.

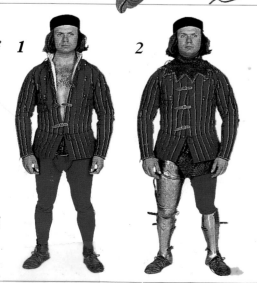

ARMOR

A suit of armor was known as a harness, and a man who wore one was called a man-at-arms. There were no high-quality armorers (armor makers) in England at this time, so armor was imported from Italy and Germany. Arms fairs were held in Europe, where armor and weapons could be bought. This is how a suit of armor was worn:
1 An arming doublet is worn to make the armor more comfortable.

2 Greaves *are worn on the shins,* poleyns *on the knees,* cuisses *on the thighs, as well as mail* braies *(like shorts). A mail* standard *is worn around the neck.*
3 The breastplate *covers the chest and* besagues *protect the armpits.*
4 Upper and lower cannons *protect the arms, with* couters *on the elbows.*
5 Pieces of shoulder armor are called pauldrons. *An arming cap makes the helmet more comfortable.*

1

2

RIGHT: *Edmund is carrying a pole axe. His usual weapon, a bill, is a long pole with a blade and a hook on the end.*

RAISING ARMIES

At the time of the Wars of the Roses, the law said that all men must own as much armor and weapons as they could afford and be prepared to serve as soldiers for 40 days every year. Noblemen like Sir Thomas Burgh were asked to provide a certain number of soldiers, many of whom were their servants. Edmund the billman is one of Sir Thomas's cooks. He wears a *jakke*. These jackets, made of as many as 30 layers of linen, were the cheapest and most common form of armor. The bowl-like object hanging from his belt is a buckler. These were worn as small shields to protect the hands, but they could also be used to hit people. Some bucklers had spikes on them.

Richard Calle owns a small piece of land near Sir Thomas's estate. In return for protection against his enemies, Richard has agreed to fight for Sir Thomas whenever necessary. He is wearing woolen hose, a mail shirt, and a jacket with Sir Thomas's livery (colors) of blue and white.

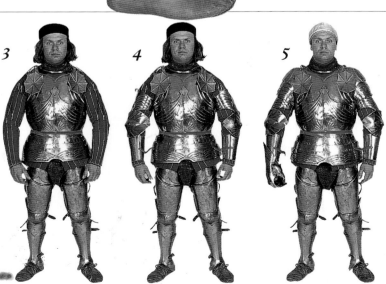

3   4   5

RIGHT: *Full armor, including a* sallet *(helmet) and* gauntlets *(armed gloves). A bevor* covers *Sir Thomas's chin and throat. The visor of the helmet can be pulled down to protect his eyes* (below).

CAVALIERS AND ROUNDHEADS

Cavalier comes from the Spanish word *caballero*, meaning mounted soldier. The name therefore suggested that the person was foreign, and it was very insulting to call a Royalist soldier a Cavalier.

Parliamentarians were called Roundheads, suggesting that they were apprentices, who had to wear short hair. Although many men on both sides wore their hair long at this time, it was very rude to call someone a Roundhead because it signified that he was a working person of low social status.

FOOD
The daily ration of marching food was one pound of round biscuits or bread and one pound of cheese or meat to eat with them. Soldiers were given knapsacks to carry their food but no plates or cutlery, so they brought their own.

Nehemiah is a tradesman and a supporter of Parliament who volunteered to join the army. His coat and shoes were issued to him, but he has supplied the rest of the uniform himself. Over his shoulder he wears an orange sash to show that he supports the Earl of Essex. If he did not wear this, it would be impossible to tell him from a Royalist sergeant.

ENGLISH CIVIL WAR 1642–60

Sergeant Nehemiah Wharton (Parliamentarian)

A civil war is a war between different groups of people within the same nation. This war broke out because the Royalists and the Parliamentarians had different views about the government and religion of England. The Parliamentarians felt that the king should have less power and Parliament more. The Royalists claimed that the king, Charles I, had been chosen by God to rule. Although, like most of England, Charles I was Protestant, his queen, Henrietta Maria, was Catholic, and many people were suspicious that he favored Catholics and foreigners. The Parliamentarians thought that English people should be Protestant. The argument between the Parliamentarians and the Royalists turned into a conflict after the Parliamentarians had Charles I's chief minister executed and the king tried to arrest five of the leading Parliamentarians.

RIGHT: *This gun is a matchlock musket. The match, or piece of rope* (shown here), *was boiled in saltpeter and then lit and applied to the priming powder so that the gun could be fired. However, the match often went out when it rained. Muskets were heavy and usually placed on rests for firing, like the one shown here.*

RIGHT: *A halberd, which is a spear fitted with an axe head, a sword, and a scabbard*

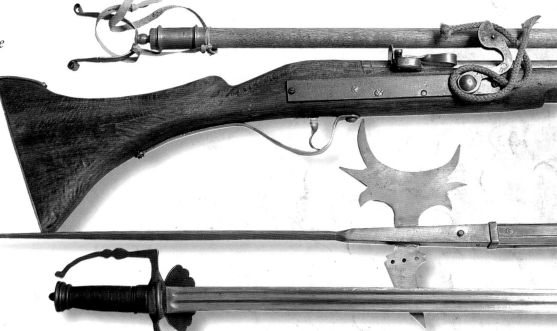

THE NEW MODEL ARMY

When the Civil War broke out, there were fewer than 500 trained soldiers in England, so thousands of civilians were either encouraged or forced to enlist. The Parliamentary army was commanded from 1642 to 1645 by Robert Devereux, Earl of Essex—only about half of the English aristocracy supported the king. Many of the regiments were led either by lords or by M.P.s (Members of Parliament) such as Denzil Holles, in whose infantry regiment Nehemiah Wharton served.

The New Model army was created in the spring of 1645 for two reasons. The first was to establish an army with professional officers, rather than lords or M.P.s commanding the men, and regular pay for all the soldiers. The second was to defeat the Royalist forces—which happened at the battle of Naseby in June 1645. The New Model army was commanded by Sir Thomas Fairfax and his second-in-command, Oliver Cromwell (*shown top center*).

Richard (seated) at the end of a day's traveling. The infantry could travel roughly 8 miles a day, and the cavalry 12 miles. At night, the infantry stayed in towns and villages, but the cavalry camped wherever they could find food and water for their horses, which was often far out in the country. Everyone had to meet the next morning before they could move on again, so progress was slow.

Soldiers often had haircuts to prevent lice from nesting in their hair.

Richard has soldier servants, who look after him and his horses. The more important an officer was, the more servants he had. Generals traveled around in carriages with their wives.

ENGLISH CIVIL WAR 1642-60

Captain Richard Atkins (Royalist)

Friends and families fought each other during the Civil War. Some people were confused because, although they supported Parliament, they felt it was their duty to be loyal to the king.

Although Parliamentarians tended to be more religious than Royalists, they did not all think that enjoyment was sinful. Most soldiers welcomed the chance to smoke a pipe and have a game of chess on a traveling set like the one shown here *(right)*.

After winning at the battles of Marston Moor (1644) and Naseby (1645), the New Model army seized King Charles I, whom they imprisoned and executed in 1649. His son was crowned King Charles II by Royalist supporters in Scotland, and he raised an army, which was defeated by the Parliamentarians. In 1653, Oliver Cromwell was appointed to rule England under the title of Lord Protector. When he died in 1658, his son took over for only a short time before Parliament voted for the restoration or return of King Charles II, who was welcomed into London with great rejoicing in May 1660.

RIGHT: *A horseman's weapons were a sword and two pistols. This is a wheel-lock pistol: When it was fired, the wheel spun around and struck against a piece of stone, so that sparks ignited the powder.*

FIGHTING

At the start of a big battle, the two armies faced each other on the field. Both armies had battle plans their generals had drawn up, showing where each part of the army was positioned. Usually, the infantry was in the middle, with cavalry on each side. First, soldiers fired the cannons, and then the cavalry charged, hoping to scatter the enemy cavalry and chase them away. If the cavalry were well disciplined, they would turn around and attack the enemy infantry.

While the cavalry were fighting, the infantry would begin to advance, firing their muskets. The aim was to break up the other line before engaging in hand-to-hand combat. First, they used the points of their pikes; then, they fought with their swords and the butts of their guns, which they used as clubs.

Sometimes the men fought until they were exhausted, but if neither side managed to chase the other off the field, both sides claimed a victory, although neither had really won.

LEFT: *Richard Atkyns was a country gentleman. When the war broke out, he used his own money to arm 60 cavalry troopers and led them into battle in Prince Maurice's Regiment of Horse. He is dressed to go into battle, wearing a helmet, buff-colored coat, breeches, and bucket-top boots. This is exactly the same as the uniform of a Parliamentarian captain, and in spite of the red sash he wears around his waist, Richard could easily be confused with one. He is wearing a bunch of leaves in his helmet as a sign to the other Royalist soldiers, so that they will know that he is on their side and not attack him during the battle.*

AMERICAN REVOLUTION 1775-83

Private James Boswell and Sergeant Richard Laird

In the 17th century, Britain founded colonies on the east coast of America. Called the thirteen colonies, they were ruled by Britain and paid taxes to the British government. In the 1760s, the colonists were angered by demands for higher taxes, especially since they were not represented in the British Parliament. They began to protest, and in 1775, war broke out between the colonists and the British troops. Thomas Jefferson wrote a Declaration of Independence stating that the colonists wanted to govern themselves. It was signed on July 4, 1776.

Although the British won some early battles, they lost many men. The colonists won important victories at Princeton and Saratoga (1777) and in 1778, France and Spain gave their support to them. The final defeat of the British at Yorktown in 1781 led to recognition of the colonists' independence and their new name, the United States of America.

ABOVE: *James's tinderbox. The glass on the lid of the box could be held up to the sun with a piece of newspaper or tinder (see page 7) beneath it. The action of the sun on the glass made the newspaper heat up, and after a while it caught fire.*

Soldiers on both sides plaited their hair or tied it back in a pigtail. For parades, they greased their hair with fat and covered it with flour or white powder.

James Boswell joined the army in June 1776. Compared to the British soldiers, he was issued very little equipment: a musket, cartridge box, bayonet, belt, and coat. He had to bring his own shirt, breeches, socks, and shoes.

James's coat is known as a lottery coat. There was often a shortage of uniforms during the war, and a lottery would be held among the soldiers to see who would get them.

THE CONTINENTAL ARMY

At the start of the war, the colonists did not have an army. Instead, they had a system by which any man between the ages of 16 and 60 could be asked to serve for short periods of time in the state militia, using weapons brought from home. Although these men fought bravely, they did not have proper training or discipline. It soon became clear to George Washington, their commander in chief, that, if the colonists were to defeat the British army, they needed a regular army of their own. He persuaded Congress to require each state to provide a number of soldiers for the Continental Army.

EATING AND SLEEPING

Soldiers were divided into units of 5 or 6 men who ate together and shared a tent. They were called messmates. Each group of messmates was given an iron cooking pot, which was suspended over a fire. There were no official army cooks. The man who was the best cook in the group usually had the job of preparing supper, which was often a stew made out of rations and anything else available. The cooking pots were very heavy and were often thrown away by soldiers on a long march.

In order for all the men to fit into the tent, they lay across its width. The most senior soldier slept at the back of the tent, so that he would not be interrupted as the other men got up to take their turn at guard duty during the night.

CLOTHING

Richard Laird (*see left*) wears a cap made of boiled leather with a horsehair crest. He needs new breeches, but because of the shortages he will have to wear his old ones until they fall apart. He wears spatterdashes (gaiters) to prevent his shoes from getting wet.

James Boswell's cartridge box, his powder horn, which is marked with his name, and a brush for cleaning out the pan after he has fired

When a flintlock weapon is fired, the flint held in the jaws of the cock hits the frizzen (the L-shaped piece in front of it), and the powder in the pan (see page 21) is struck by sparks. These cause the powder inside the gun to explode, firing the ball out of the muzzle.

Corporal Naylor and Private Fell in full marching order, ready to go on campaign. Soldiers were known as redcoats because of their uniforms. All soldiers wore black felt cocked hats trimmed with lace and a regimental button. Around the soldiers' necks were stocks, which kept their heads up and were very uncomfortable.

FOOD

Basic military rations *(below)* were bread, cheese, and meat, which had to be cooked by the soldier himself. Sometimes, there was an issue of rice, oats, or even vegetables, which could be used to make a stew. Although they risked a flogging if they were caught, soldiers would steal potatoes, carrots, and corn *(above)* from nearby fields. The wooden canteen carried water, although this was not really safe to drink, and soldiers were often given beer or tea instead.

Inside every soldier's knapsack was a spare shirt to wear on Sundays, a blanket, food, and personal items such as a shaving brush and penknife.

RIGHT: *Shoes did not have left and right feet, so the soldiers reversed them each day.*

AMERICAN REVOLUTION 1775–83

Corporal George Naylor and Private James Fell

Like many soldiers, James Fell was a farm laborer before he joined the 47th Regiment of Foot. One autumn, when the harvest was finished, James could not find any work, but then he met Corporal Naylor and decided to join the army. When war broke out in America, James was told that his regiment would have to go there. The reason for the fighting was that America, then a British colony, wanted to be independent, and Britain wanted to continue governing it. James did not want to travel 3,000 miles from home, spending about three months in the hold of a sailing ship, and he thought of running away, or deserting. But then, he had to watch while a soldier who had deserted and been caught was given 500 lashes with a whip called a cat-o'-nine-tails. James decided that going to America was better than risking such a flogging.

FIGHTING

Soldiers on both sides began the battle by firing at each other and then charging with bayonets. Neither side was able to aim their guns accurately if the target was more than 100 yards away, so they waited until the enemy was as close as possible before firing. British regiments usually formed a long, two-man line, with one man kneeling and one man standing behind him. The line was split into groups called platoons. Each platoon was told to fire at a different time so that the line was always defended.

Whether he meant to or not, a man joined the army and took his first day's pay by merely touching the king's shilling. Because of this rule, some men were tricked into 21 years of army service by shaking hands with a soldier who had a shilling hidden in his palm.

IN BATTLE

Loading the guns. Private Fell bites off the end of his cartridge paper.

Corporal Naylor puts some powder from his cartridge paper in the pan. Then the men drop the rest of the powder and the ball down the gun barrels.

Corporal Naylor uses his ramrod to push the powder and ball down into the barrel.

The soldiers pull back the flints and release them, firing the guns.

After firing several times, they charge.

NAPOLEONIC WARS 1799-1815

Private John Green (British) and Sergeant Dominique Courvoisier (French)

Napoleon Bonaparte took control of the French government in 1799. He wanted to conquer Europe, India, the Carribean, and the Middle East. In 1804, he proclaimed himself French Emperor and planned to invade Britain. Although Admiral Nelson defeated his navy at the battle of Trafalgar in 1805 and prevented the invasion, Napoleon's armies did invade Germany, Portugal, and Spain. A British army was sent to Portugal in 1808 to help expel the French. By the end of the Peninsular War (1808–1814), the French army had been driven back into France. Napoleon invaded Russia in 1812, but it was a disaster, with 600,000 soldiers dying, most from cold and hunger. In 1813, his army was defeated by Russian, Prussian, and Austrian forces at Leipzig. In 1814, the Allied armies invaded France, and Napoleon was exiled to Elba island. In March 1815, he escaped and raised a new army, which was defeated by British, Prussian, and Belgian forces at the battle of Waterloo in 1815. This time, Napoleon was exiled to St. Helena island in the South Atlantic.

ABOVE: *Soldiers were issued mess tins, but they had to provide other personal items themselves.*

The bugle on the shako *(hat) is the light infantry's symbol. The regimental colors of the 68th Durham Light Infantry were red and green. Red was a traditional color for soldiers' jackets, which were made of wool. The lace sewn onto the jacket front has red and green thread running through it.*

JOINING THE ARMY

John Green joined the the army in 1806 because he could not get work as a farm laborer. His pay—one shilling a day, with nine pence kept back for expenses—is less than a laborer's, but it is better than starving. He enlisted for 7 years, even though it meant that he would not get a pension unless he was wounded (men who enlisted for life got a pension when they retired).

John carries a blanket, a knapsack, a water canteen, a ration bag, and a cartridge box. Soldiers, carrying all this equipment, sometimes had to march 60 miles in the space of 24 hours.

Sergeant Dominique Courvoisier of the 21ième de Ligne (21st Line Infantry)

Dominique's calfskin pack contains his eating equipment, which includes a small frying pan and some spare clothes. Napoleon's military tactics depended on having fast-moving armies. Since food wagons slowed the army down, soldiers often were not given rations and had to find their own food.

LEFT: *The gold stripe on Dominique's lower arm shows that he is a sergeant, and he has two red chevrons, each representing seven years' service.*

NAPOLEON'S ARMY

There were three types of infantry regiments in Napoleon's army: guard, light, and line. Originally, the light infantry had done a job similar to that of Roman auxiliaries *(see page 4)*, namely engaging in skirmishes (short fights) and keeping the enemy at bay until the army was ready to attack. But by the time of the Napoleonic Wars, the line infantry had its own light infantrymen, and there was little difference between them. The guard were the elite infantrymen.

The line infantry had three types of soldiers: grenadiers (the tallest and strongest men, who were regarded as the best), the voltigeurs (light infantrymen), and the fusiliers (musketeers) like Dominique.

Dominique's cartridge box is decorated with an "N" (for Napoleon) and a crown. He carries a Charleville flintlock musket, and he can carry a sabre (curved sword) because he is a sergeant. These were called sabres-briquets. *They were generally considered useless for fighting but good for chopping up firewood.*

AMERICAN CIVIL WAR 1861-65

Private Rap Lee Cathey (Confederate) and Private Walter Plumb (Union)

In the United States in the 1850s, the Southern states became unhappy with laws imposed on them by President Lincoln's government, and they wanted the power to govern themselves. By early 1861, 11 Southern states had broken away from the Union and become the Confederated States of America. They formed a government, elected a president, and set up an army.

The Northern and Southern states had quarreled over many issues, but the two most important ones were trade and slavery. Owning slaves was allowed in the South, but some people in the North thought that the slaves should be set free. These people were called abolitionists.

In many ways, the American Civil War was the first modern war. It was the first time in a conflict that messages were sent by telegraph, the first time troops were transported to battle by train, and the first time that machine guns were used.

ABOVE AND RIGHT: *Sutlers, or military provisioners, sold items like these to the men. Some things, like the housewife or sewing set* (shown right) *were useful, but soldiers threw others away when they proved too much to carry on the march.*

ABOVE: *Knapsack, blanket, tent section, and spare underwear. The Southern states had strong links with England, where they exported a lot of cotton. Some items of Confederate kits, such as this knapsack, were made in England.*

MOTIVES

Rap Lee Cathey (*opposite, kneeling*) of the 2nd Virginia Infantry enlisted in April 1861, the first month of the war. Like most Americans, he thought that the war would soon be over. But after the first big battle, it became clear that the fighting would continue for some time. Rap, like many Confederate soldiers, comes from a farming family. Since he does not own slaves himself, Rap is not concerned about preserving slavery, but he does not like people from the North telling him what to do.

Walter Plumb of the 119th New York Volunteers (*opposite, standing*) enlisted in 1862. The army was offering a bounty of $250, and since Walter's wife was expecting a baby, he needed the money. Although some of his fellow soldiers are abolitionists, Walter is not concerned about ending slavery. He thinks that the Southern states are insulting the American flag by trying to break away and govern themselves.

Both armies had a good postal system. Walter and Rap write home regularly.

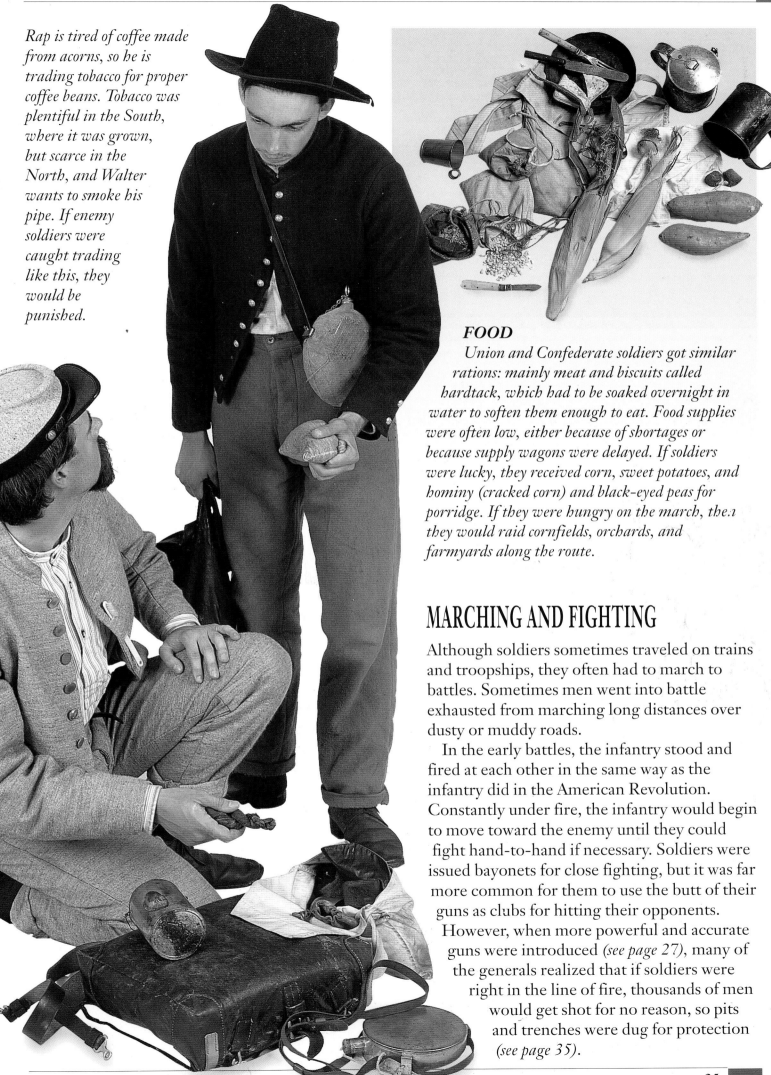

Rap is tired of coffee made from acorns, so he is trading tobacco for proper coffee beans. Tobacco was plentiful in the South, where it was grown, but scarce in the North, and Walter wants to smoke his pipe. If enemy soldiers were caught trading like this, they would be punished.

FOOD

Union and Confederate soldiers got similar rations: mainly meat and biscuits called hardtack, which had to be soaked overnight in water to soften them enough to eat. Food supplies were often low, either because of shortages or because supply wagons were delayed. If soldiers were lucky, they received corn, sweet potatoes, and hominy (cracked corn) and black-eyed peas for porridge. If they were hungry on the march, the.1 they would raid cornfields, orchards, and farmyards along the route.

MARCHING AND FIGHTING

Although soldiers sometimes traveled on trains and troopships, they often had to march to battles. Sometimes men went into battle exhausted from marching long distances over dusty or muddy roads.

In the early battles, the infantry stood and fired at each other in the same way as the infantry did in the American Revolution. Constantly under fire, the infantry would begin to move toward the enemy until they could fight hand-to-hand if necessary. Soldiers were issued bayonets for close fighting, but it was far more common for them to use the butt of their guns as clubs for hitting their opponents. However, when more powerful and accurate guns were introduced *(see page 27)*, many of the generals realized that if soldiers were right in the line of fire, thousands of men would get shot for no reason, so pits and trenches were dug for protection *(see page 35)*.

CASUALTIES

Wounded men usually received treatment on the battlefield before being sent to makeshift hospitals set up in nearby houses or schools. Anesthetic was used, but the doctors did not clean their instruments or change their bloodstained clothes between operations. They did 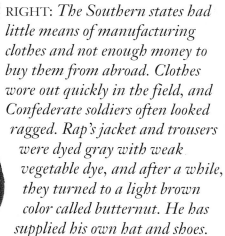 not know that they were spreading germs and causing infections. For example, wounded limbs were usually amputated and the wound often became infected, killing the patient. More than half of the war casualties were not from injuries but from diseases like dysentery and typhus, which are caused by germs. There were no proper toilets in the soldiers' camps, and conditions were not much cleaner in the hospitals.

Since soldiers did not wear dog tags, it was hard to identify dead bodies on the battlefield unless they had letters or photographs in their pockets. Some soldiers even wrote their names on pieces of paper and pinned them to their clothes. Roll calls were taken after battles, but the army did not always know what had happened to the missing men.

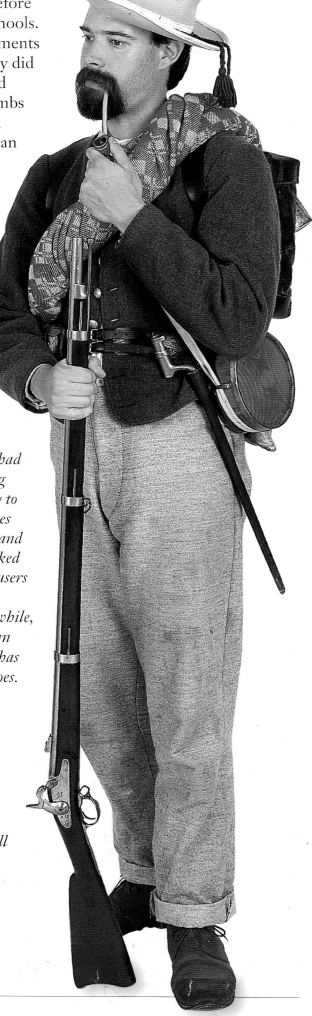

RIGHT: *The Southern states had little means of manufacturing clothes and not enough money to buy them from abroad. Clothes wore out quickly in the field, and Confederate soldiers often looked ragged. Rap's jacket and trousers were dyed gray with weak vegetable dye, and after a while, they turned to a light brown color called butternut. He has supplied his own hat and shoes.*

LEFT: *Rap carries a knapsack, haversack, wooden water bottle, cartridge box, and bayonet. A blanket roll is slung across his shoulder. Beneath the blanket roll is a tin pot for making coffee.*

LEFT: *Walter wears a dark blue jacket and sky-blue trousers, both woolen. In winter he wears a blue overcoat (see far right).*

RIGHT: *On his left hip, Walter carries a fabric-covered metal water bottle and a bayonet scabbard. On his back is a knapsack, a rolled-up blanket, and a cartridge box.*

FIRING BY FILE
When soldiers were suddenly confronted by the enemy, they stood in two ranks and fired by file. The first two men would fire, then the second two, and then the third, and so on down the line.

Emptying the powder and lead ball from the cartridge into the gun's muzzle

Pushing them down the barrel with the ramrod

Placing the percussion cap on the nipple

Firing the guns

MUSKETS

Although some new weapons were introduced during the Civil War, the chief weapon for both armies was the musket *(see right and below)*, which was produced either by the Springfield armory in Massachusetts or by the Enfield Company of Great Britain. These had been improved since the time of the American Revolution by adding a percussion cap. This was a small copper cap *(see right)* that fitted over a little knob called the nipple. When the gun was fired, the hammer hit the percussion cap, and the sparks set off the powder inside the gun and fired it.

BELOW: *A musket, bayonet, and cartridge box with cartridges, and a three-pronged tool used to repair the musket. Muskets were now rifled, which meant that there were spiral grooves inside the barrel. These grooves made the ball spin as it flew out of the gun, making it more accurate over a longer distance.*

THE INDIAN WARS 1854-90

Bad Hand (Cheyenne Warrior) and James H. Thomas (Buffalo Soldier)

At the start of the 19th century, Native tribes lived on the central plains of North America. Among these tribes, known as Plains Indians, were the Cheyenne, whose territory formed parts of Montana, Wyoming, and Colorado. There were 12 main tribes of Plains Indians, including the Sioux, the Blackfeet, and the Crow, and they often fought each other in order to capture horses and secure hunting grounds with plenty of buffalo. War was important to them: The way for a man to gain respect was to be brave in battle *(see opposite)*.

In the 1840s and '50s, white Americans began to leave the eastern states to claim land in the West. In the early years of this westward movement, the Natives traded with those who crossed their territory but otherwise ignored them. However, misunderstandings led to the massacre of a Sioux village, which was the start of more than 30 years of wars between Natives and the U.S. Army. By 1890, the Natives' way of life was destroyed, and the tribes were forced to live in small areas called reservations.

ABOVE: *Items acquired in raids or by trading:* (clockwise from left) *a porcupine-tail brush, a bag made from a cavalryman's boot, a burning glass (magnifying glass) for lighting fires* (see page 18), *tinted glasses, tweezers, and a mirror.*

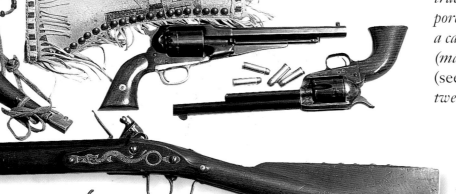

FIGHTING

The Natives did not have an army. When they fought other tribes, only small numbers of men were involved, and what mattered most was the bravery of individual warriors. Their ideas about war did not include military discipline, with soldiers obeying orders, and they had never fought against large numbers of troops like the U.S. Army. Traditionally, many tribes were enemies, so different tribes rarely banded together to fight the army.

Natives knew they needed guns *(see above left)*, not bows and arrows, to fight the army, and every warrior wanted one. Some of the most common were *(top)* revolvers like the .44 Remington and the .45 Colt, which was used by the U.S. Army; *(center)* the musket; and *(bottom)* the .44 Henry. A decorated holster and a powder horn are also pictured. Guns were often decorated with brass studs.

BELOW: *For hunting buffalo, bows and arrows were better than guns because they were silent and didn't scare away the animals.*

COUNTING COUP

Men who had gained battle honors, or coups, by displays of bravery were highly respected. Coups could be earned in several ways. The most common was deliberately to touch an enemy—either with the hand or with a weapon or stick held in the hand—without harming him. Taking an enemy's horse or gun was a major coup, but in many tribes, killing an enemy was only a minor coup. Coup marks, like war medals, showed the bravery of the wearer. A warrior of high status had the right to wear a warbonnet, or feathered headdress (see page 30).

Shields were believed to have spiritual and physical power to prevent their owners from being wounded.

Ready for battle. Bad Hand's horse Wapaha (Warbonnet) wears a necklace strung with U.S. Army cartridges and scalps. His ears have been slit to show that he is a warhorse, and his nostrils are painted red to make him look fierce.

One of the coup marks on Wapaha's legs is red, because Bad Hand was wounded when he counted his coup.

The Indian wars were fought on horseback. A good warrior like Bad Hand might have as many as 25 horses, but only one was strong, brave, and fast enough to be a warhorse. The red markings on his body show where he has been wounded in previous battles.

Bad Hand is wearing special clothes for the ceremony before a battle. His warbonnet and ceremonial lance show that he has high status in his tribe.

Bad Hand's sleeves are decorated with hair from enemies killed under his command. Often, enemies were scalped because hair was considered part of a person's spiritual power and removing it took power away from him.

Leaders of war parties carried pipes. Warriors who smoked the leader's pipe in a prebattle ceremony accepted his leadership for that battle.

When Bad Hand was 15, he acted as water carrier on his first war party, but by 17, he was considered to be a warrior. When he reaches 40, he will stop going to war because he will have gained enough coups to have high status in the tribe.

MEDICINE

Native Americans believed that everything in the world was part of one Great Spirit and was a source of spiritual power, or "medicine." There were many kinds of medicine: The sun, moon, earth, and sky all had special power. Medicine protected warriors in battle. It was acquired in visions — for example, warriors painted their shields with symbols from their dreams so that they would not get killed in battle.

LEFT: A buffalo robe with a pictogram of a battle, with (clockwise from left) bags of red and yellow war paint; a tobacco twist, pouch, and pipe; an arrow for tamping down the tobacco in the pipe; a buffalo shoulder bone tobacco-cutting board; and sacred herbs.

BUFFALO SOLDIERS

At the end of the Civil War (see page 24), most of the soldiers who remained in the U.S. Army stayed on in the Southern states. After a few months, the government realized that soldiers were needed to fight in the Indian wars, and new regiments were formed. They were commanded by white officers but made up entirely of black soldiers. The Natives called these men buffalo soldiers because their hair looked like the thick coat of the buffalo. Although slavery had been ended by the Civil War, racist laws and attitudes meant that black men had little chance of education and few career opportunities. The army offered education, a career, and a retirement pension. Soldiers enlisted for five years, and black regiments had the highest reenlistment rate in the army and the lowest desertion rate. The pay was small, but black and white soldiers received the same.

Buffalo soldiers served from the Canadian to the Mexican borders of America. They were usually stationed at forts, living in barracks. When they were not in combat, they helped to build frontier forts and put up telegraph lines.

ABOVE: *Within 10 years of joining the army, James H. Thomas had been promoted to Quartermaster Sergeant, the highest rank a black soldier could hold. His job was to make sure that the soldiers had the right equipment. It involved a lot of paperwork and could be done only by an educated man.*

EQUIPMENT

The government outfitted new regiments in leftover Civil War uniforms (see page 26). Soldiers had white gloves, which they wore to collect their pay. They were issued Springfield "trap door" rifles (see right). These were Civil War muzzle-loading guns that had been changed into breech-loaders (see page 46). At this time, it was against the law for a black civilian to own a gun.

Arthur always carries his pay book, which records the details of his army service and how much he is paid. If he is killed, it will help to identify his body. Soldiers can choose to have some of their pay sent home to their families.

Arthur's pack weighs 60 lbs when it is full. His mess kit, for cooking and eating, is on the outside in a cloth cover.

Arthur was issued this leather jerkin the first winter that he was in the trenches, to help him keep warm.

The diagonal band on Arthur's cuff is a good-conduct stripe. Below it, he has a metal woundstripe. Arthur's wound was a "blighty one." This meant that it was severe enough for him to be sent back to England for treatment. When it healed, he was ordered back to the trenches to continue fighting.

WORLD WAR I 1914-18

British, German, French, American, and Australian Soldiers

Before World War I, the three great powers of western Europe—Britain, France, and Germany— were competing to be the strongest country with the largest empire. In eastern Europe, there were two vast empires: Russia and Austria-Hungary. These five nations formed two alliances: Germany and Austria-Hungary on one side, called the Central Powers; and France, Britian, and Russia on the other, called the Allies.

Germany planned to declare war on France, defeat it, and then attack Russia, which had a larger army. But, when the Germans marched into Belgium, the British, who had promised to help if Belgium was invaded, declared war on Germany. When war broke out, Arthur Fisher, like many other British men, volunteered. They were eager to fight for their king, George V, and country, and were afraid that if they delayed, they might miss the war. The British thought that Germany would soon be defeated and that the war would be over by Christmas. Arthur left his job to enlist, and after training in England, he was sent to the Western Front, which ran through Belgium and France.

Although Arthur is used to trench life (see page 35), he hates not being able to wash and having lice. Arthur burns the louse eggs in his clothes with a candle and squashes the adult lice, but it only takes a few days before he starts to itch again.

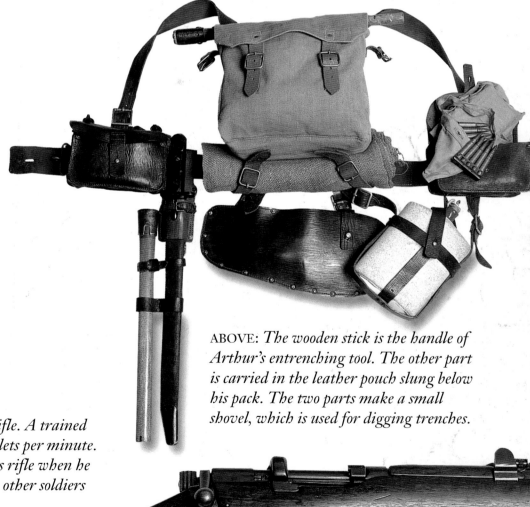

ABOVE: *The wooden stick is the handle of Arthur's entrenching tool. The other part is carried in the leather pouch slung below his pack. The two parts make a small shovel, which is used for digging trenches.*

BELOW: *Short magazine Lee Enfield rifle. A trained soldier can fire more than 15 aimed bullets per minute. Arthur fixes his bayonet to the end of his rifle when he advances across no-man's-land with the other soldiers to attack the enemy.*

TRENCH WARFARE

The method of fighting used on the Western Front was trench warfare. Trenches were long, narrow ditches dug about 10 feet deep. British and French trenches stretched across France and Belgium, often only a few yards away from the German trenches. The land between the enemy trenches was called no-man's-land.

If the generals decided to attack, the artillery would fire thousands of shells across no-man's-land to try to kill as many of the enemy as possible. The soldiers were then told to assemble in one part of the trench. When the signal was given, the soldiers had to scramble out and run across no-man's-land as fast as they could to try to capture the enemy trenches. As they ran, the enemy fired at them. During these attacks, thousands of soldiers were killed in a few minutes.

Besides artillery and machine-gun fire, soldiers were also killed by poison gas. The attacking soldiers opened up gas cylinders, and the wind blew the gas toward the enemy trench. However if the wind blew in the wrong direction, the attackers might end up gassing themselves. Gas blinded, burned, and killed soldiers.

LEFT: *Early gas masks were chemical-soaked cloth bags* (top, center), *which did not work well. Later ones* (below) *had air filters.*

FOOD

Arthur's mess kit and food rations. Rations consisted of bully beef (corned beef) and hard biscuits. Rations also included cans of stew, which often had to be eaten cold, and tea, which was brewed behind the lines by army cooks and brought up to the trenches in big vats. The kit roll shown here contains Arthur's knife, fork, and spoon, his razor, shaving brush, button-stick, and comb.

A British trench store containing canned food and a Tommy's cooker. The big jar is full of rum, which was given to soldiers in cold weather or before an attack.

RAIDING PARTY

Sometimes at night, small bands of soldiers went on raiding parties to the enemy trenches to get information about what they were planning to do next. They cut through the barbed wire in no-man's-land with wire cutters like the ones shown (*left*). Raiding parties were very dangerous, and the soldiers who took part in them were usually volunteers.

LEFT: *British entrenching tool, wire cutters, and a rattle, which was used to warn the men to put on their masks when there was a gas attack*

RIGHT: *German Musketier (Musketeer) Kasmir Heska of the 63rd Infantry Regiment carrying his Mauser 7.92mm caliber rifle. When the war started, Kasmir was an army reservist, which meant that he had done military service and could be called up if Germany went to war. France also used reservists, but Britain relied on volunteers until 1916, when the government introduced conscription.*

TRENCH LIFE

Soldiers in World War I spent more time digging and repairing trenches than fighting. Continuous shelling, digging, and heavy rain turned large areas of France and Belgium into a swamp, full of water-filled craters. All the soldiers found the trenches very uncomfortable places to live because they were muddy and smelly, with nowhere to wash and little food. It was not unusual for soldiers to be up to their knees in water, and there were no proper toilets. In some places, unburied and rotting dead soldiers lying on the ground beside the trench made it stink and caused the spread of disease. Soldiers were normally in the trenches for less than a week at a time, before being sent back to safer areas behind the lines for one or two weeks to rest, train, and prepare for another turn in the trenches.

CASUALTIES

Every soldier carried a field dressing to try to stop the bleeding if he was wounded. Wounded men often took refuge in shell craters, but they might have a long and agonizing wait before a stretcher party reached them. If many men were wounded, stretcher parties were told to bring back only those who had a chance of recovery.

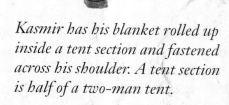

Kasmir has his blanket rolled up inside a tent section and fastened across his shoulder. A tent section is half of a two-man tent.

LEFT: *Kasmir is ready to attack, with his bayonet fixed to his rifle, and wearing his helmet, which is painted in dazzle camouflage. Although soldiers on both sides did a lot of bayonet practice during training, most of the casualties were caused not by bayonets but by artillery, rifle fire, or gas.*

ATTRITION

By 1916, generals on both sides could see that, with soldiers in entrenched positions, the war was not going to end by one side winning a definite victory over the other in battle. As a result of this, they decided that the soldiers should not give up any ground, no matter how many were killed. This tactic is called attrition, which means wearing down. Although the generals knew that many of their men would die in this process, they figured that, as long as the enemy lost more men than they did, they would win the war. Probably the best

example of this took place at Verdun, a French fortress near the German frontier. The Germans knew that Verdun was important to the French, and they calculated that for every two German soldiers who died attacking it, five French soldiers would die defending it. They were wrong—the battle of Verdun lasted 10 months, and although the French suffered 362,000 casualties, the Germans suffered 336,800. The battle of the Somme and the third battle of Ypres, also known as Passchendaele, produced even more casualties. There were 20,000 British dead and 35,000 wounded on the first day of the Somme alone.

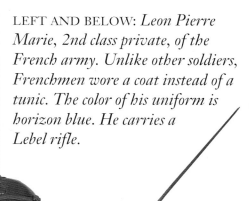

LEFT AND BELOW: *Leon Pierre Marie, 2nd class private, of the French army. Unlike other soldiers, Frenchmen wore a coat instead of a tunic. The color of his uniform is horizon blue. He carries a Lebel rifle.*

RIGHT: *U.S. Staff Sergeant John J. Hincky carrying his Springfield rifle*

ABOVE: *In World War I, American soldiers were called doughboys because they said that their packs looked like lumps of dough and would be as useless as lumps of dough on a battlefield!*

GALLIPOLI

Although most of the fighting in World War I took place in Europe, there was also action in Turkey, the Middle East, Africa, and China. Turkey joined the Central Powers in November 1914 *(see page 33)*. By 1915, the British commanders had formed a plan to attack Germany through the Balkans. In April 1915, Allied troops, including the Australian and New Zealand Army Corps (ANZACs), landed at Gallipoli. The attack was unsuccessful because Turkish troops on the cliffs above the beach made it impossible for the Allies to move anywhere without heavy losses. It turned into trench warfare, which was made worse by hot weather and outbreaks of cholera and malaria. By October 1915, when most of the Allies withdrew, about 36,000 soldiers had been killed.

Australian uniforms, designed for the battlefield rather than the parade ground, were more comfortable than British ones.

THE END OF THE WAR

America had supplied the Allies with weapons since the war began, but many Americans felt that they should not fight, even though the German U-boats (submarines) were sinking their ships. In 1915, a British passenger ship, the *Lusitania*, was torpedoed and many Americans died.

In January 1917, British Naval Intelligence decoded a telegram from Germany offering Mexico the return of Texas, New Mexico, and Arizona if it would fight against America. America therefore declared war on Germany in April 1917. Although regular American soldiers were sent to France immediately, it took a year to train the volunteers, who arrived in Europe in early 1918. America had large numbers of men, and German manpower and supplies were running short. With America's help, the Allies broke through the German lines, and some German soldiers refused to go on fighting. On November 11, 1918, Germany signed an armistice, agreeing to stop fighting and discuss peace.

Private George Hayward of the 4th Battalion Australian Imperial Force. George volunteered because he wanted to help defend the British Empire.

George Hayward is wearing a slouch hat. These were given to ANZAC troops to wear in hot climates. After Gallipoli, George's unit fought on the Western Front. They were given steel helmets to replace their slouch hats.

Infantrymen at Gallipoli often wore scraps of white cloth to help the commanders see how the attack had advanced. It was also important for the artillerymen to be able to see the infantry so that they would not fire at them by mistake.

American soldiers were called G.I.s. The initials stood for General Issue.

American uniforms were olive drab. German ones were field gray.

WORLD WAR II 1939-45

German, American, French, British, Russian, and Japanese Soldiers

War broke out in September 1939 when Adolf Hitler, the German leader, ordered his army to invade Poland. They used a new type of warfare, sending in tanks and aircraft to break through the Polish defenses and following them up with infantrymen. It was called blitzkrieg (lightning war).

When Hitler refused to withdraw from that country, Britain, France, Australia, New Zealand, and India (the Allies) declared war on Germany. The Soviet Union (Russia) joined the Allies in June 1941, after Hitler's troops had marched across the Russian border. Both Italy and Japan made alliances with Germany, and these three countries were called the Axis. America joined the Allies in December 1941, after the Japanese attacked the U.S. airbase at Pearl Harbor.

Unlike previous wars, this was total war, involving both soldiers and civilians. Fighting took place in almost every part of the world, and of the 55 million people who died, around 30 million were civilians.

ABOVE: Yank *magazine was produced in America for soldiers fighting abroad.*

LEFT: *Frederick surrenders to Norman. Norman looks at Frederick's Soldbuch (pay book) to check his identity before handing him over to the military police. Frederick will be sent to a prisoner of war (POW) camp in America until the war is over.*

ABOVE: *This German machine gun with its ammunition belt and boxes is an MG 34. MG stands for* Maschinengewehr *(machine gun).*

CONSCRIPTS AND VOLUNTEERS

Frederick Gockel was a student in Hanover, Germany, when he received his call-up papers in the winter of 1944. After basic training, he was sent to one of the new Volksgrenadier divisions, which Hitler intended to use in his attack against the Americans in the Ardennes, Belgium. Although this attack was successful to begin with, by January 1945, the Americans, with their greater manpower, had halted it.

Frederick has been taken prisoner by Private Norman Padgett of the U.S. 4th Infantry Division. When the war started in Europe, Norman thought that the Americans should not become involved in it, but as soon as he heard about the attack on Pearl Harbor, he volunteered. He thought he would be sent to fight the Japanese and was surprised when he ended up in Europe instead.

THE WAR IN EUROPE

In April 1940, the Germans invaded Norway, Denmark, the Netherlands, and Luxembourg. They marched through Belgium to invade France. Like the Poles in 1939, the French army of 1940 was not prepared for the Germans' blitzkrieg style of warfare, and northern France was soon under German occupation.

The British Expeditionary Force (B.E.F.), which had been sent to France in 1939, became trapped in northern France by the advancing German forces. In May 1940, both the B.E.F. and other Allied troops had to be rescued from the beaches of Dunkirk and brought back to England by a variety of British naval and civilian vessels ranging from warships to yachts.

In June, the French head of state Marshal Pétain signed an armistice *(see page 37)* with Germany. He moved his government to Vichy, a town in the part of France that was not occupied by German troops until 1942. Although their government cooperated with the Germans, many French people joined the resistance movement known as the *Maquis*, which helped in the fight against Germany. General Charles de Gaulle refused to accept the armistice signed by Pétain and formed a group of soldiers who continued to fight with the Allies against Germany. Called the Free French, they were based in England.

LEFT AND BELOW: *Pierre Blanc, 2nd class private. Pierre's uniform is khaki, but very similar in design to the World War I uniform, and his weapon is still a Lebel rifle* (see page 36).

RIGHT: *Private William Linton. William was drafted in 1940, just before the Germans invaded France.*

BOMBING

William is worried about the safety of his wife, who lives in London and is in danger from German air raids. By 1939, airplane technology was much improved from World War I, and all the major powers had air forces. Airplanes were used in battles such as the battle of Britain (1940) and also to drop bombs on both military and civilian targets. Often, soldiers fighting abroad were in less danger than their families at home.

ABOVE: *William's equipment is similar to that carried by British soldiers in World War I: an entrenching tool, a shovel, a water bottle, a pack, and a Lee Enfield No.4 rifle.*

PERSONAL KIT

William and his fellow soldiers were issued mess cans, rations, and washing and shaving kit. Soldiers who took part in the D-Day invasion were given a French guidebook and money. Next to these are the identity disks that British soldiers wore around their necks. They were marked with the soldier's name, rank, army number, and religion.

D-DAY

By June 1940, the Allies began making plans to free the German-occupied European countries. It took four years to plan, but by 1944, Britain was full of Allied soldiers, sailors, and airmen waiting to invade France on D-Day, June 6. The date was kept secret, and the Germans were taken by surprise. In August, the German commandant in Paris surrendered, and by spring 1945, British and American troops had begun to advance on Germany. Russian troops *(see page 42)* began advancing on Germany through Austria, and by early April, they had captured the capital, Vienna. On April 25, the Russian army surrounded Berlin. Hitler committed suicide on April 30, and on May 7, Germany surrendered. May 8 was declared VE (Victory in Europe) Day.

LEFT: *Private Linton is wearing woolen khaki-colored battle fatigues, a steel helmet with a camouflage cover, and hobnail boots.*

ABOVE: *All soldiers had first-aid training and carried field dressings like these.*

RIGHT: *The Bren gun* (top) *was the light machine gun used by British soldiers. It fired 500 rounds per minute. The Sten submachine gun* (bottom) *was also widely used.*

THE EASTERN FRONT

Hitler invaded the Soviet Union in June 1941. His invasion plan was called Operation Barbarossa. At first, the invading German army, supported by Panzer (tank) divisions and the Luftwaffe (air force), made fast progress. However, winter began before the Germans arrived in Moscow, and although the troops came within 19 miles of the city, the very cold weather and strong Russian defenses prevented them from capturing it.

Operation Barbarossa was ruined, but fighting continued in the Soviet Union, especially around the cities of Stalingrad and Leningrad, both of which were besieged by the Germans. The assault on Stalingrad took place in August 1942. But although the Germans moved easily through the city's outskirts, the Russians defended every building in the center, forcing the German army to fight its way from house to house. While this was happening, a Soviet counterattacking force gathered outside the city. They surrounded and bombarded the German army until it surrendered in January 1943.

The siege of Leningrad lasted from September 1941 until January 1944, during which time about 1 million people in the city died, many from starvation and disease. Eventually, the Soviet army drove the Germans from the city, which was given the title Hero City because the inhabitants had defended it so bravely.

RIGHT: *Soviet Army Sergeant Vassili Valentinov. When the Soviets were attacking, the well-trained tank and artillery divisions broke through the enemy lines, followed by huge numbers of infantrymen, who killed as many of the enemy as they could.*

Vassili has a PPSh-41 submachine gun. PP stands for pistolet pulyemet, *meaning machine pistol.*

U.S. Marines (see opposite) used Thompson submachine guns, known as Tommy guns. American helmets had the special feature of a fiber lining, which could be removed. The helmet could then be filled with water for washing and shaving.

LEFT: *Soviet infantry soldiers were often badly trained and undisciplined. They sometimes went for as long as three weeks without receiving rations, and they had to live off the land. When the supplies arrived, there was a vodka ration as well as food.*

THE WAR IN THE PACIFIC

This war began in December 1941. When the Japanese attacked two British colonies, Malaya (now Malaysia) and Hong Kong, and launched a surprise attack on the Pearl Harbor U.S. Naval Base, the United States and Britain declared war on Japan. At first, Japanese forces controlled the Pacific, and by early 1942, they had occupied many of the nearby islands and invaded Burma. Expansion was halted when the Japanese were defeated by the U.S. Navy, and U.S. forces gradually began to recapture the islands. The best-known island is Iwo Jima, which was important because it provided a base for American bombers to make raids on Japanese cities. U.S. forces, including the 4th Marine Division *(see below)* captured it in March 1945.

The war in the Pacific ended two months after the war in Europe, when the U.S. Air Force dropped atomic bombs on the Japanese cities of Hiroshima and Nagasaki (August 6 and 9). Japan surrendered on August 14, and the next day, Americans celebrated VJ (Victory over Japan) Day.

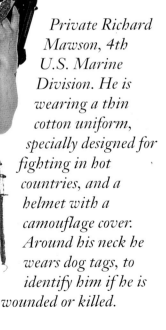

Private Richard Mawson, 4th U.S. Marine Division. He is wearing a thin cotton uniform, specially designed for fighting in hot countries, and a helmet with a camouflage cover. Around his neck he wears dog tags, to identify him if he is wounded or killed.

ABOVE: *Gurkha Havildar (Sergeant) Dhan Bahadur Rai. Besides his gun, he carries a kukri, or curved knife, which is useful both for cutting through the jungle and as a weapon. Gurkhas, who were recruited into the British army from Nepal, served in Burma, which meant enduring a hot climate, months of continual rain, and dense jungle.*

LEFT: *Japanese Private First Class Renya Toyodo, in winter uniform. Renya is proud to be serving Emperor Hirohito. Hirohito had the status of a god, and soldiers considered it an honor to sacrifice their lives for him.*

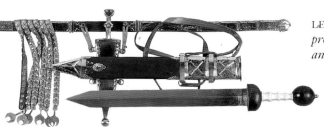

LEFT: *Roman soldier's belt with protective bronze apron, sword, and dagger*

RIGHT: *Sergeant Richard Laird, American soldier in the American Revolution*

TIME LINE

509 B.C.	Rome becomes a republic.
58–51 B.C.	Julius Caesar conquers Gaul.
43 B.C.	Claudius conquers Britain.
c.122 A.D.	Hadrian's Wall is built in Northern Britain. Roman Empire is at its height.
476 A.D.	Last Roman Emperor is deposed.
800–1100	Viking raids on Europe: Vikings settle in Britain and France.
1066	✗ Hastings. Duke William of Normandy is crowned William I.
1096–99	First Crusade
1147–49	Second Crusade
1187	Muslims recapture Jerusalem.
1191–92	Third Crusade
1202–04	Fourth Crusade

1337–1453   Hundred Years War

c.1340	Cannon first in use
c.1380	Handguns first in use

1455–85   The Wars of the Roses
Important events:

1460	✗ Northampton, Wakefield
1469	✗ Edgecote
1471	✗ Barnet
1485	✗ Bosworth
1500	Wheel-lock mechanism is first fitted on handguns.

1642–60   English Civil War
Important events:

1642	✗ Edgehill
1644	✗ Marston Moor
1645	✗ Naseby
1649	Execution of Charles I
c.1650–1700	European armies adopt guns with flintlock mechanism.
c.1650	Bayonet is invented in Bayonne, France.
c.1700	Bayonet in general use

1775–83   American Revolution
Important events:

1775	✗ Lexington, Concord, Bunker Hill
1776	✗ Trenton
1777	✗ Saratoga
1780	✗ Charleston
1781	✗ Yorktown

1799–1815   Napoleonic Wars
Important events:

1805	✗ Trafalgar
1808–14	Peninsular War
1812	Napoleon invades Russia.
1815	✗ Waterloo
1832	American Samuel Colt patents design for revolver.

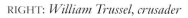

RIGHT: *William Trussel, crusader*

LEFT: *Bullets, American Civil War*

RIGHT: *Sergeant Elsie Pannell, British Auxiliary Territorial Services, World War II*

1861–65   American Civil War
Important events:

1861	✕ First Bull Run (Manassas)
1862	✕ Antietam
1862	✕ Shiloh
1863	✕ Gettysburg

1862   American Richard Gatling patents first machine gun.

1864   The Red Cross Society is founded to care for war casualties.

1867   Swedish Alfred Nobel manufactures the explosive dynamite.

1854–90   Indian Wars
Important events:

1876   ✕ Little Big Horn
1890   ✕ Wounded Knee

1867   Barbed wire is patented.

1882   Field telephones first in use

1883   American inventor Hiram Maxim introduces the first fully automatic machine gun.

1903   American Wright brothers make the first powered aircraft flight.

1914–18   World War I
Important events:

1914   ✕ The Marne
German invasion of France is halted.

April 1915   German army uses gas for first time at Ypres. By September, the Allies are using gas.

1915   The Gallipoli campaign
1916   ✕ Verdun
1916   ✕ The Somme
Tanks are used for the first time, by the British army.

1917   ✕ Passchendaele (Third Battle of Ypres)
U.S.A. joins the Allies.

1918   Armistice Day (November 11th)

LEFT: *Bad Hand, Cheyenne warrior, Indian Wars*

1939–45   World War II
Important events:

1940   Dunkirk evacuation of France
Battle of Britain

1941   Germans invade U.S.S.R.
Pearl Harbor
U.S.A. joins Allies.
In Britain, conscription of women is introduced for the first time. They must serve in the Auxiliary Services, or on farms, or work in factories making weapons.

1942   ✕ El Alamein
✕ Coral Sea and Midway

1944   D-Day (June 6th)

1945   Allies invade Germany.
VE (Victory in Europe) Day (May 8th)
Major U.S. air offensive against Japan
American flyers drop atomic bombs on Hiroshima and Nagasaki
VJ (Victory in Japan) Day (August 15th)

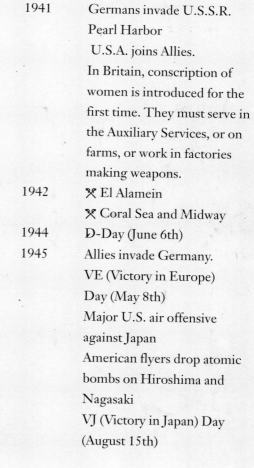

GLOSSARY

Artillery Originally, an artillery piece was a weapon that fired heavy missiles, such as large cannon balls. The word artillery is now used to describe any gun of higher calibre (*see below*) than a machine gun.

Auxiliary A soldier who has a supporting role. Auxiliaries in the Roman army supported the legionaries by skirmishing with the enemy until the army was ready to attack. Female soldiers in the British Auxiliary Territorial Service during World War II supported the male soldiers but were not allowed to fire guns themselves. Auxiliary soldiers may be mercenaries (*see below*) in the service of a foreign government.

Barracks A building or group of buildings that soldiers live in

Barrel The tubular part of a gun, from which the bullet or shell is fired

Bayonet A short blade that can be fixed to the muzzle of a gun

Bombardment A prolonged and intense attack using artillery (*see above*)

Breechloader Any firearm in which the shell or bullet is loaded from behind the barrel, as opposed to a muzzle loader (*see below*).

Calibre The diameter of a shell or bullet. For example, British rifles and machine guns in both World War I and II used .303 inch calibre ammunition.

Camouflage A disguise using paint or parts of natural things such as leaves and branches so that soldiers can blend in with the surroundings and not be spotted by the enemy

Cartridge A metal or paper tubular case that contains the explosive charge for a weapon. It usually contains the shell or bullet as well.

Conscription Compulsory military service. Conscripts are men (and occasionally women) who have been ordered to join the army. This often happens when a country is involved in a conflict- for example, there was conscription in Great Britain during World War II.

Crusade Any war that is fought for a religious cause—the term crusade particularly refers to military expeditions to the Holy Land made in the 11th, 12th, and 13th centuries in order to capture the city of Jerusalem and the land surrounding it from the Muslims.

Enlisting Joining the army. A man originally wrote his name, or if he could not write, put his "mark" on a list to show that he had joined.

Fatigues A soldier's job that does not involve fighting and is usually domestic. Soldiers are sometimes put on fatigues as a form of punishment. The term is also used for the clothing that soldiers wear when they are doing these jobs.

File A line of soldiers standing one behind the other

Infantry Soldiers who fight on foot

Lace Colored tape or braiding on soldiers' uniforms that identifies the regiment in which they serve

Machine gun An automatic weapon which is capable of continuous fire. Early machine guns were heavy and difficult to move around, and during World War I the light or submachine gun, which could be carried by one man, was introduced.

Mail An early form of armor made from interlocking rings of metal

Mercenary A soldier hired to fight for a foreign army, who fights for money, rather than loyalty to that particular country or ruler

Mess This term was used to refer to a meal eaten by a group of soldiers, but now can also mean the soldiers' eating place or a group of men who normally eat together (sometimes known as messmates).

Militia An army made up of civilians who are not full-time soldiers, but who have enlisted to serve only during emergencies

Musket A long-barreled, muzzle-loading gun

Muzzle-loader Any firearm in which the shell or bullet is loaded from the front end of the barrel, or muzzle

Pan Pan-shaped area at the breech of a muzzle-loading gun where a small amount of priming powder is placed to ignite the main charge in the barrel and cause the gun to fire

Priming Powder Fine gunpowder that is placed in the pan of a musket to set off the main charge in the barrel

Ramrod A long wooden or metal pole that is used to push the bullet down the barrel of a muzzle-loader.

Rank A line of soldiers standing side by side. The term rank also refers to a soldier's position within the army (e.g., sergeant, corporal).

Regiment A military unit consisting of 800 to 1200 soldiers

Revolver A firearm with revolving chambers inside, which allows several bullets to be loaded at once, so that the gun can be fired repeatedly without reloading

Rifle A long-barreled firearm with spiral grooves inside the barrel, which make the bullet or shell spin as it is shot out of the gun. This makes the gun more accurate over a longer range.

Saltpeter Another name for the chemical compound potassium nitrate, which is used in the manufacture of gunpowder

INDEX

PLACES TO VISIT

Antietam National Battlefield
P.O. Box 158, Sharpsburg,
Maryland 21782-0158
Tel: 301/432-5124

Appomattox Court House National
Historical Park
P.O. Box 218, Appomattox, Virginia 24522
Tel: 804/352-8987

Colonial Williamsburg Foundation
Williamsburg, Virginia 23187
Tel: 1-800-HISTORY

Colorado History Museum
1300 Broadway, Denver, Colorado 80203
Tel: 303/866-3682

Cowpens National Park
P.O. Box 308, Chesnee,
South Carolina 29323
Tel: 803/461-2828

Fort Donelson National Park
P.O. Box 434, Dover, Tennessee 37058
Tel: 615/232-5706

Fort Laramie
P.O. Box 86, Fort Laramie, Wyoming 82212
Tel: 307/837-2221

Fort Ligonier
Routes 30 & 711, Ligonier,
Pennsylvania 15658
Tel: 412/238-9701

Fort Necessity National Park
R.D. 2, Box 528, Farmington,
Pennsylvania 15437
Tel: 412/329-5512

Fort Washington
13551 Fort Washington Road, Fort
Washington, Maryland 20744
Tel: 301/763-4600

Gettysburg National Park
97 Taneytown Road, Gettysburg,
Pennsylvania 17325
Tel: 717/334-9410

Harpers Ferry Historical National Park
P.O. Box 65, Harpers Ferry,
West Virginia 25425-0065
Tel: 304/535-6029

Kennesaw Mountain National Park
900 Kennesaw Mountain Drive, Kennesaw,
Georgia 30144-4854
Tel: 404/427-4686

Little Big Horn National Monument
P.O. Box 39, Crow Agency,
Montana 59022-0039
Tel: 406/638-2621

Manassas Battlefield
6511 Sudley Road, Manassas,
Virginia 20119-2005
Tel: 703/754-1861

Minuteman National Historical Park
174 Liberty, Concord, Massachusetts 01742
Tel: 508/369-6993

Moores Creek National Park
P.O.Box 69, Currie, North Carolina 28435
Tel: 910/283-5591

Nez Perce National Historical Park
P.O. Box 93, Spalding, Idaho 83551-0093
Tel: 208/843-2261

Old Barracks Museum
Barrack Street, Trenton, New Jersey 08608
Tel: 609/396-1776

Petersburg National Battlefield
1539 Hickory Hill Road, Petersburg,
Virginia 23803-4721
Tel: 804/732-3531

Saratoga National Historical Park
648 Route 32, Stillwater,
New York 12170-1601
Tel: 518/664-9821

Shenandoah National Park
3655 U.S. Highway 211 E., Luray,
Virginia 22835
Tel: 540/999-3500

Shiloh National Park
Route 1, Box 9, Shiloh, Tennessee 38376
Tel: 901/689-5696

Stones River National Park
3501 Old Nashville Highway, Murfreesboro,
Tennessee 37129
Tel: 615/893-9501

Tupelo National Battlefield
2680 Natchez Trace Parkway, Tupelo,
Missouri 38801
Tel: 1-800-305-7417

Valley Forge National Historical Park
P.O. Box 953, Valley Forge,
Pennsylvania 19482
Tel: 610/783-1007

Vicksburg National Military Park
Union Avenue, Vicksburg, Mississippi 39180
Tel: 601/636-0583

Wilson's Creek National Park
Route 2, Box 75, Republic, Missouri 65738
Tel: 417/732-2662

Wounded Knee Gravesite
Write to: Oglala Sioux Tribe, Pine Ridge,
South Dakota 57750 for directions

ACKNOWLEDGMENTS

Breslich & Foss would like to thank the following people for sharing their enthusiasm with us, for allowing themselves to be photographed, for lending us equipment, and for answering our questions so patiently:

pp4–5 Chris Haines, Tony Segalini, and Richard Story of the Ermine Street Guard

pp6–7 Roland Williamson of *Regalia Anglorum*

pp8–11 John Cole, John Jay Phillips, David Page, and Ian Jeremish of Conquest

pp12–13 Ian Pycroft, Mark Griffin, and Philip Allen of the Merchant's House

pp14–17 Alan Turton, Simon Frame, and Thomas Gray of the English Civil War Society

pp18–19 Edmund Moderacki, James P. Sieradzki, and James Boswell of the Brigade of the American Revolution; Richard Patterson of the Old Barracks Museum, Trenton, New Jersey

pp20–21 Gary Brierley and Alan McEwan of the 47th Regiment of Foot

pp22–23 Sean Phillips and Ian Miller of the 68th Regt. Durham Light Infantry, Mr and Mrs Phillips, and Michael Rimmer; Mike Freeman and Richard Ransome of the *21ième Regiment d'Infanterie de ligne*

pp24–27 Chris Shreiber, Sam Cathey, and Christopher Daley of the American Civil War Society

pp28–31 Michael Terry, Joe and Jean Brandl, and David Jurgella; William Gwaltney of Fort Laramie, Wyoming, and Andrew Maisich of the Colorado History Museum. Photographs on p. 31 appear courtesy of the Colorado Historical Society

pp32–43 Trevor Poole and Tom Hill of the Great War Society; Mike Barnes, Titus, Michael Johnson, Maurice Stokes; Robert Stedman, Martin Brayley, Laurent Ladrosse, Richard Ingram, Simon Vanlint, Tim Sparks, and Jumkaji Gurung; Gerard Gorokhoff, Phillipe Charbonnier, Brigadier Bullock of the Gurkha Museum, Andrew Fletcher of BAPTY, and Nick Hall of Sabre Sales, 85 Castle Road, Southsea.

pp44–45 Isabelle Campion